The McGraw-Hill Foundation Series

 PAINTING AND DECORATING

Also in this Series:

PAINTING AND DECORATING

by

Walter Chlystyk

Technical Director
South Peel Vocational School
Port Credit, Ontario

McGRAW-HILL COMPANY OF CANADA LIMITED

New York   TORONTO   London   Sydney

PAINTING AND DECORATING

Copyright © McGraw-Hill Company of Canada Limited, 1965

94628

4 5 6 7 8 9 0 B65 0

Drawings by Bernice Kikuko Iles

Printed and Bound in Canada

ACKNOWLEDGEMENTS

The author wishes to thank the following people who have helped in the preparation of this book:

Mr. J. F. McGivney, Principal of Parkway Vocational School in Toronto, whose encouragement and suggestions over the years have been invaluable;

Mr. N. Smith, of Canadian Pittsburgh Industries Ltd., who reviewed the units of this book that deal with paint;

Miss Mary Prud'homme, of Canadian Wallpaper Manufacturers Limited, who provided valuable information for the unit dealing with wallpaper; and

Mr. R. Bothwell, of Canadian Wallpaper Manufacturers Limited, whose excellent colour illustrations demonstrate colour theory so vividly.

W.C.

The colour illustrations on pages 49 to 54 are reproduced by the courtesy of Canadian Wallpaper Manufacturers Limited.

The colour illustrations on pages 55 and 56 are reproduced by permission from
The Home And Its Furnishings, First Edition
By Ruth Morton
Copyright, 1953, By McGraw-Hill Inc.

CONTENTS

1 GENERAL INFORMATION

Paint and colour have been used for decoration for at least 20,000 years. Thousands of years ago in France and Spain, men painted pictures of animals on the walls of caves. In 3000 B.C., the Egyptians and the Babylonians used yellow, red, black, blue-green, and white on walls and columns to decorate their temples and homes. Greek sculptors painted their statues in life-like colours. The Romans painted stone and plaster to look like marble. The early Christians painted religious symbols and pictures of saints on walls. About 1,100 years ago, in the Middle Ages, painters formed their own guilds of masters, journeymen, and apprentices.

In the beginning, all paint was mixed by hand on the job. As more and more people began to use paint, on-the-job hand mixing of paint stopped, and the paint industry grew. In recent years, new materials for making paint have been discovered and developed. This progress is still taking place. Modern and costly machinery is used now to produce ready-mixed paints that are far better than the old on-the-job hand-mixed paints, and much less expensive. Today, in Canada, everyone can afford a gleaming paint coating on his home.

Paint is not the only decorative material that has been used over the centuries. Wallpaper as a decoration for the home is as old as civilization. Four thousand years ago, in China, someone made the first wallpaper from the inner bark of trees. Later, in the same country, rice paper was used, on which pictures and designs were hand-painted. When the Chinese invented printing, wallpaper designs began to be printed from wooden blocks. Wallpaper, at that time, could be afforded only by the rich. Hand-painted and early printed wallpapers were very slow to produce and were, therefore, very expensive.

In 1841 A.D., C. & J. Potter, a company located near Liverpool, England, was the first firm that printed wallpaper by machine in continuous lengths. These papers, unlike the early printed wallpapers, were printed in more than one colour. The printing was done by rollers, one roller for each colour. Today, all wallpaper is manufactured by machine in a variety of colours, designs, and fabrics. Some wallpapers are still expensive, but there are very many wallpapers on the market that the average family can afford. Even these inexpensive wallpapers are better than even the best papers that only the rich could afford in the past.

WHAT PAINTERS AND DECORATORS DO

A painter and decorator is a person who puts protective and decorative coatings on the inside and outside walls and ceilings of office buildings, factories, apartment buildings, and private homes. His work is not unusually heavy. Although, at times, he must move heavy ladders, carry large containers of paint, and set up awkward and heavy scaffolding, such jobs take only a small part of his time. However, a painter and decorator must be fairly strong. He must be able to work for many hours in a standing, crouching, or reaching position. He must be able to stand heights. His wrists must be strong.

During the spring and summer months, and in the early fall, the painter is very likely to be working outside at least part of the time. Late fall and winter will find him doing most of his work indoors.

A good painter and decorator must know the product that is best suited for a particular surface. He must follow the proper steps when he does a job. He must develop his eye to be able to judge colours correctly. He must be able to estimate how much a job should cost before the job is begun. To learn these things, and many more, he must have training. For four years, he must serve an apprenticeship. Four months of this apprenticeship are spent at a trade school. At school he learns the theory of his trade, and the proper procedures to follow. During his time on the job, he learns the useful tricks of the trade.

As with every other career, there are both advantages and disadvantages to the trade of painting and decorating.

ADVANTAGES

1. There is personal satisfaction to be gained from doing a good job of painting and decorating. The painter takes pleasure in seeing unpainted surfaces take on a smooth, colourful appearance. His efforts are usually appreciated by other people.

2. He knows that buildings will last longer, and will be in better condition for living and working because of the job he does.

3. The job is seldom monotonous. The painter and decorator has the opportunity of working both indoors and outdoors. He is always creating something new.

4. His type of work keeps him in good condition. His constant movement while using brushes and rollers and climbing up and down ladders and scaffolding keeps his muscles strong and healthy.

DISADVANTAGES

1. There is some danger of falling from ladders and scaffolding.

2. The fumes of some paints can be harmful to the lungs. When these paints are used a special mask must be worn.

3. The work tends to be seasonal. In the spring, summer, and early fall, he may have more than enough work. The winter months tend to be slow.

It is up to the individual to weigh the advantages and disadvantages of painting and decorating as a means of livelihood. Anyone who does choose to master this skilled trade will find his efforts well rewarded.

2 BASIC TOOLS AND EQUIPMENT

WORDS TO LEARN

Drop Sheet — a large sheet of cloth that is placed over furniture or floor to protect it from paint and paste

Scaffold — a raised platform to support workmen and their tools

Exterior — outside

Interior — inside

Porous — full of pores, or small holes that can absorb liquids

Portable — movable

Stationary — not portable

Tapered — smoothly graduating from thick at one end, to thin at the other

In painting, as in any other trade, the tradesman must be familiar with the basic tools and equipment that he will use. Brushes, rollers, and spray guns are the tools that a painter uses to apply a finish to a surface. His other equipment includes scrapers, putty knives, ladders, drop sheets, and possibly a scaffold.

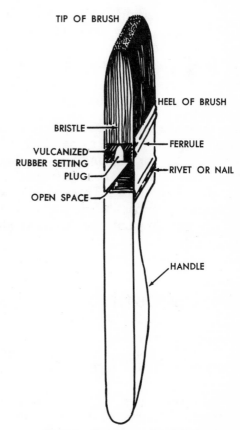

TIP OF BRUSH

HEEL OF BRUSH

BRISTLE

FERRULE

VULCANIZED RUBBER SETTING

RIVET OR NAIL

PLUG

OPEN SPACE

HANDLE

Fig. 2.1   Main parts of a paint brush

BRUSHES

Each job requires its own kind of brush. There is a wide variety of brushes available in a great range of sizes and costs. However, most brushes are made in the same way.

Main Parts of a Brush

1. The handle is usually made of wood.
2. The ferrule is a metal wrapping that holds the bristles to the handle.
3. The bristles are the part of the brush that hold the paint. There are many kinds of bristle. The type you choose will depend on the job that you are doing.
4. The divider or wooden plug is a wedge around which the bristles are fastened to form a flat or round shape.
5. The rubber setting is the rubber that holds the bristles together, and prevents their falling out of the brush.
6. Nails or rivets hold the ferrule to the handle.

TYPES OF BRISTLE

The type of bristle you choose will depend on what kind of paint you are using. A type of bristle that is good for oil paint may be ruined by water. Some bristles must be specially treated before they are used. This special treatment can make it impossible for the brush to be used with certain paints. You should know the characteristics of various bristles so that you will know when to use which type.

Hog Bristles

Hog bristles are excellent for brushing oil paints. They are available in three types, all of which have these characteristics:

(a) One end of each bristle is *flagged* (split into fine hairs). These flagged ends trap and hold the paint.

(b) The bristles are tapered. The paint runs from the thick end of the bristle to the thin end. Tapered bristles spring back into

shape after they have been bent.

(c) The bristles are oval in cross section.

(d) The surface of the bristle is covered with pores that help to trap and hold the paint.

| Tientsin | Hankow | Chunking |

Fig. 2.2   Types of Chinese hog bristle

Nylon Bristles

Brushes with nylon bristles are especially useful in water paints. In the past, nylon bristles were unsuitable for use in oil paints. Today, nylon bristle brushes are becoming widely accepted in place of hog bristle brushes for applying oil paint. This change is caused by a number of factors.

1. Since most of the hog bristles used for making brushes comes from China, the supply is very uncertain. As the supply gets smaller, the cost gets higher. Nylon bristles can be made very cheaply.

2. New manufacturing methods produce nylon bristles that match the characteristics

of hog bristle. Old style nylon bristles did not have flagged ends, and had no pores. The result was that the bristles were not able to hold the paint.

3. Nylon bristles need no pre-conditioning.

For applying water paints, nylon bristle brushes are used almost exclusively. There are several reasons for this fact.

1. Nylon does not absorb water. Hog bristles will go limp and useless if they are used in water paints. Water is absorbed into the bristle through the pores. When the water is absorbed, the hog bristle swells, and becomes useless.

2. Nylon bristles are easy to clean. Hog bristles have scales that trap paint, whereas nylon bristles are smooth. Running water washes away excess paint from nylon very easily.

Other Types of Bristles

1. Horsehair bristles are used to make dust brushes and floor-sweeping brushes.

2. Sable bristles are used to make artists' brushes and lettering brushes.

3. Camel-hair bristles are used to make varnish brushes, lacquer brushes, and high-gloss enamel brushes. Although called camel hair, the bristles actually come from a kind of squirrel that lives in Siberia.

ROLLERS

In the last few years, rollers have become very widely used tools for painting. Paint rollers can be used to apply both interior and exterior oil and water paints. Rollers are ideal for painting large areas and hard-to-reach surfaces. If a long handle is attached to the handle of a roller, ceilings and walls can be painted without having to use a stepladder or scaffold.

The two main parts of a roller are the handle and the sleeve. Some sleeves simply slip onto the frame of the roller handle. This type of sleeve is called a slip-off sleeve. Other sleeves have nylon ends that are held on the handle by a screw or nut. This type of sleeve is called a rod and nut sleeve. Roller sleeves may be made from any of the following materials:

1. *Mohair.* A wool-and-cotton fibre, green in colour, and close-cropped to a uniform length of pile.

2. *Lambswool.* Pure wool, forming a fairly long and shaggy pile.

3. *Dynel.* An imitation lambswool, more efficient than lambswool with most paint on most surfaces.

4. *Plastic foam.* A layer of fine sponge, excellent for applying semi-gloss and high-gloss paints.

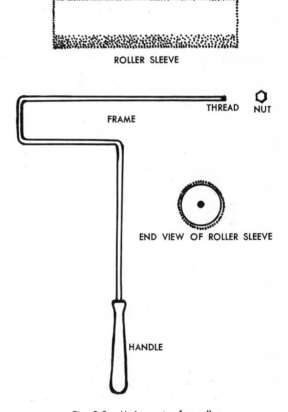

ROLLER SLEEVE

END VIEW OF ROLLER SLEEVE

Fig. 2.3 Main parts of a roller

Types of Rollers

1. The most commonly used roller is the dip-type. The roller is dipped into the paint that has been poured into a roller pan. To make sure that the paint is evenly distributed on the sleeve, the roller is rolled along the shallow end of the pan. This action also removes excess paint from the sleeve.

Fig. 2.4   Dip type roller

2. The fountain type of roller is filled by pouring the paint into the roller. When the sleeve is pressed against a surface, the paint seeps through the sleeve.

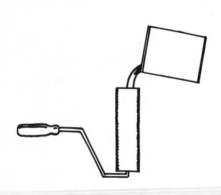

Fig. 2.5   Fountain type roller

3. The pressure type of roller is filled by air pressure forcing the paint through the handle of the roller into the sleeve. When the sleeve is pressed against a surface, the paint seeps through the sleeve.

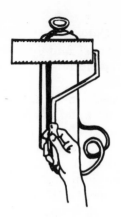

Fig. 2.6   Pressure type roller

SPRAY PAINTING EQUIPMENT

Some surfaces can be painted with spray equipment more easily and cheaply than with brush or roller. Some paint materials and some lacquers must be sprayed, because they dry so quickly. A painter must know the different types of equipment that are available, and the best type of equipment to use for a particular job.

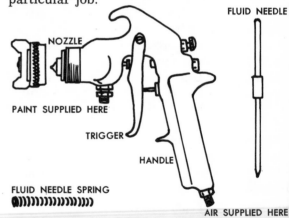

Fig. 2.7   Main parts of a spray gun

Types of Spray Guns

There are two types of spray guns.

1. The suction feed type of spray gun works by using a vacuum to suck paint out of the paint container. Once the paint is sucked

up, it is forced through the nozzle of the gun by a stream of air. Figure 2.8 shows how the gun works.

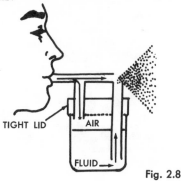

TIGHT LID   AIR

FLUID

Fig. 2.8

2. The pressure feed type of gun works by air pressing on the surface of the paint. The paint is forced up out of the cup or container, and then is forced through the nozzle of the gun by a stream of air. Figure 2.9 shows how the gun works.

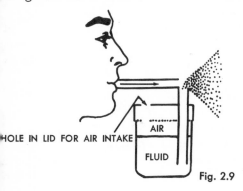

HOLE IN LID FOR AIR INTAKE   AIR

FLUID

Fig. 2.9

Spray Gun Nozzles

In both types of gun, the spray is formed by the paint mixing with the air. This mixing is done by the nozzle. There are two different types of nozzle.

1. External mix nozzles mix the paint with the air outside the cap of the nozzle. These nozzles are especially recommended for fast-drying materials such as lacquer. If the lacquer mixes with the air inside the nozzle, the lacquer may dry and clog the fluid tip hole.

External mix nozzles can be used with both types of gun.

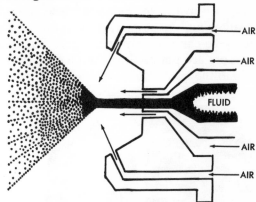

AIR

AIR

FLUID

AIR

AIR

Fig. 2.10a   External mix nozzle

2. Internal mix nozzles mix the paint and air inside the cap of the nozzle. This type of nozzle is best used with slow-drying enamels. Internal mix nozzles can be used only with the pressure feed type of gun.

Figure 2.10 shows how each type of nozzle works.

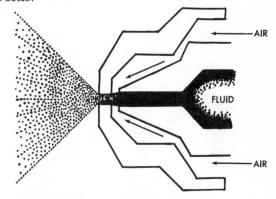

AIR

FLUID

AIR

Fig. 2.10b   Internal mix nozzle

Air Compressors

In spraying paint, a constant supply of air is needed to force the paint out of the paint container, through the paint gun, and onto the surface being painted. To supply this air under pressure, an air compressor is used. Air compressors are available in several sizes and types.

1. For small jobs, such as spraying a table or a box, small, portable electric compressor units are available. Because these units are small enough to be carried by hand, they can easily be carried from job to job. Such compressors are powered by the electricity available in the home.

Courtesy De Vilbiss (Canada) Limited

Fig. 2.11   Small portable air compressor

2. For large jobs, such as spraying large surfaces like walls, large, portable electric and gas operated compressors are available. These compressors are too heavy to be carried, but are supplied with wheels so that they can be moved to the job.

Courtesy De Vilbiss (Canada) Limited

Fig. 2.12   Large portable air compressor

3. In some large factories, such as furniture factories and automobile plants, large, stationary compressors are used to supply the air for spraying.

Courtesy De Vilbiss (Canada) Limited

Fig. 2.13   Stationary air compressor

ASSIGNMENT

1. What are the three basic tools a painter uses to apply paint?
2. What are the main parts of a brush?
3. Name three kinds of bristle.
4. What kind of bristle is best for use in oil paint?
5. What kind of bristle is best for use in water paint?
6. Why are nylon bristle brushes becoming popular for use in oil paint?
7. Name three types of roller.
8. Draw and label a diagram of one type of paint roller.
9. What kinds of materials are used to make roller sleeves?
10. What kind of roller sleeve is best for applying gloss paints?
11. Name two kinds of spray gun.
12. Draw a diagram of one kind of spray gun.
13. There are two types of spray gun nozzles. Name them, and tell which nozzle is used with which type of gun.
14. What is the purpose of an air compressor?
15. What kind of air compressor is used for small jobs?

3 USING AND MAINTAINING PAINTING EQUIPMENT

WORDS TO LEARN

Solvent — a liquid that dissolves something

Technique — a way of doing something

Tradesman — a worker who has a special trade, such as a painter and decorator

Excess — extra; more than enough

Slight — little

Eliminate — get rid of

Flow Out — spread after being applied to a surface

Prevent — make sure that something does not happen

Restore — repair

Set Up — form a skin after being applied to a surface

Suspend — hang up

Orange Peel — the surface of paint or varnish that has dried too fast after spraying

In order to do a good job, a tradesman must use good tools. The use of poor tools will result in a poor job. Good tools cost money. The most economical tools are good ones that are properly used and well cared for.

BREAKING IN A NEW BRUSH

Except for nylon brushes and brushes that will be used in shellac or lacquer, all new brushes should be pre-conditioned, or broken in, before they are used. This pre-conditioning is especially necessary for hog bristle brushes. New paint brushes, no matter how well they are made, can be ruined if they are not properly prepared before they are used in paint. By following a few simple steps, you can increase the life of a brush, and obtain better finished surfaces.

Steps in Breaking in a New Brush

1. Remove the wrapper and draw the bristles through your hand to remove any loose bristles. Tapping the bristles against the palm of the hand will also help to remove loose bristles.

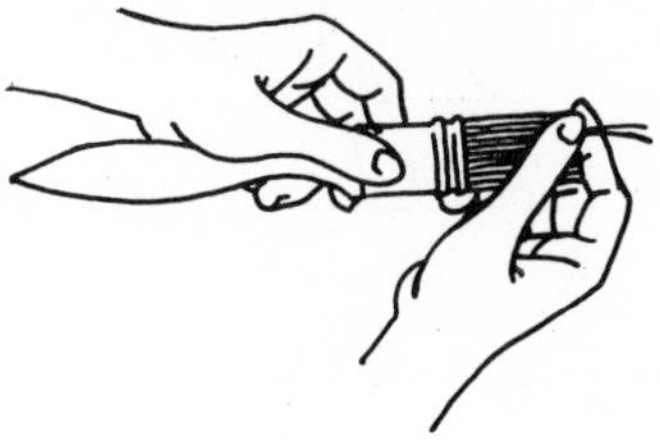

Fig. 3.1a

9

2. Replace the wrapper and suspend the brush in raw linseed oil for about two days. Do not let the bristles touch the bottom of the container.

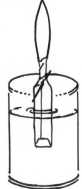

Fig. 3.1b

3. Remove the wrapper, and squeeze as much oil as possible from the bristles.

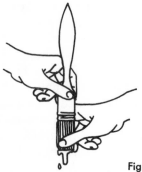

Fig. 3.1c

4. Whirl the brush between your palms to spin out more oil.

Fig. 3.1d

5. Dip the bristles into turpentine several times. Squeeze out the turpentine.

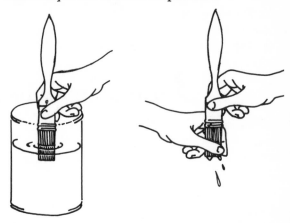

Fig. 3.1e   Fig. 3.1f

6. Comb the bristles straight.

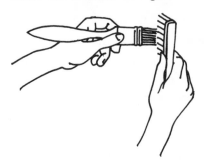

Fig. 3.1g

The linseed oil that the porous hog bristles absorb seals the bristles against thinners and moisture. This sealing prevents the bristles from becoming soft and flabby. Soaking a brush in linseed oil also makes the bristles easier to clean. Paint does not harden as readily on brushes that are treated in oil.

Fig. 3.2a   Unsealed hog bristle

Fig. 3.2b   Sealed hog bristle

Points to Remember About
Pre-Conditioning New Brushes

1. Do not pre-condition brushes that are to be used in paints that do not contain oil.

2. Do not pre-condition brushes that will be used in shellac or lacquer. Any oil that is on the bristles will ruin the shellac or lacquer finish.

BRUSHING TECHNIQUES

For easy brushing when painting most surfaces, hold the brush as you would a pencil. Use a free, easy movement of the arm and wrist.

When the temperature is too low, oil paints will not flow out, and brush marks will show. When the temperature is too high, the paint will set up too fast, and will not flow out. Not only will brush marks show, but the paint will wrinkle, crack, and peel as well.

Brushing Water Paints

1. Water paints, such as casein and latex paints, do not flow out as well as most oil paints. This fact means that water paints will leave brush marks. In order to overcome this problem, apply these paints with a semi-circular motion. This motion, known as half-moon-

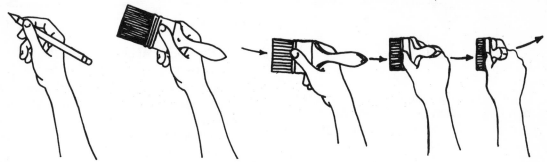

Fig. 3.3 How to hold a paint brush

Brushing Oil Paints

1. Thin primers for new wood according to the manufacturer's directions. Primers are brushed right into the surface of the wood to provide a good base for the following coats of paint. Use a worn brush for applying primers. Finish brushing with the grain of the wood.

2. Apply enamel undercoats a little more heavily than primers. Allow undercoats to flow out to eliminate brush marks. A slightly worn brush is better than a new brush for applying undercoats.

3. Apply enamels and varnishes with a new, soft, tapered brush. These paints are flowed on rather than brushed into the surface.

Do not apply oil paints when the temperature is less than 65°F., or more than 80°F.

ing, will not eliminate brush marks, but will make them far less noticeable.

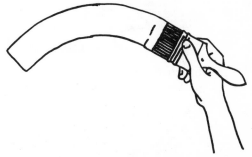

Fig. 3.4 Half-mooning

2. On narrow surfaces, such as casings and baseboards, this half-mooning technique cannot be used. Apply the paint as heavily as possible to hide the surface. Do not apply the paint so heavily that sags or runs result.

Steps in Brushing Paint

1. Dip about one-third of the length of the bristles into the paint. If you dip any more than one-third of the bristle length into the paint, the paint will collect in the heel of the brush. Any paint in the heel will tend to harden, and will be hard to clean out of the brush.

Fig. 3.5a

2. Tap the bristles against the side of the paint pot. This action removes excess paint and prevents paint from dripping off the brush.

Fig. 3.5b

3. The brush should meet the surface at an angle no smaller than 45°.

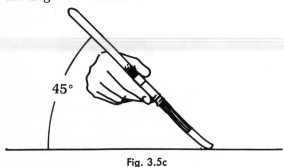

45°

Fig. 3.5c

4. Two-way brushing will result in a smooth, even finish. First, brush the paint across the grain of the wood. Then, with the tip of the brush, finish brushing with the grain of the wood. This final operation is called tipping, or laying off.

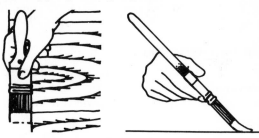

Fig. 3.5d Two way brushing   Fig. 3.5e Tipping off

Points to Remember About Brushing Paint

1. Start with a clean brush.

2. Apply as much paint as possible to as small an area as possible without allowing runs or sags.

3. If the surface to be painted is too narrow to allow brushing across the grain of the wood, apply the paint with the longest possible stroke.

4. Some paints require slight thinning to make brushing easier. Thinning will help the paint to flow out.

5. Always keep a wet edge. If the paint is allowed to dry before the job is finished, lap marks will show where the dry paint is overlapped by the wet paint.

6. When painting wood, finish with the grain to help eliminate brush marks.

7. When painting with casein or latex paints, wash the brush with water from time to time to prevent the paint from drying in the heel of the brush.

HOW TO CLEAN PAINT BRUSHES

A paint brush can easily become a useless tool if it is not cleaned properly after use. It is far easier and wiser to clean a brush immediately after use than to try to restore it if paint has been allowed to dry in it.

Steps in Cleaning a Paint Brush

1. Remove excess paint from the brush by squeezing the paint out of the bristles with a flat piece of wood.

Fig. 3.6a

2. Wash the brush in the proper solvent.
3. Spin out the excess solvent.

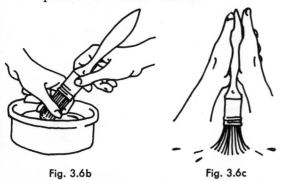

Fig. 3.6b   Fig. 3.6c

4. If the brush is not going to be used for some time, wash it in a mild solution of soap and water. Rinse the brush in clear water,

shake out excess water, and comb the bristles straight with a brush comb. Allow the brush to dry, and then wrap it in heavy paper. Hang the brush on a hook, or lay it flat.

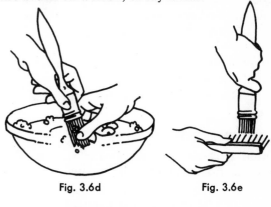

Fig. 3.6d   Fig. 3.6e

Fig. 3.6f

DO'S IN USING A BRUSH

1. Use the proper size of brush for the job.
2. Turn the brush in your hand between strokes, to prevent one side of the bristles' wearing out faster than the other side.
3. Always wash the brush thoroughly after using it.

DON'TS IN USING A BRUSH

1. Never leave a brush standing on its bristles.
2. Never leave a brush soaking in water.

TYPES OF PAINT AND THEIR CLEANING SOLVENTS

TYPE OF PAINT	CLEANING SOLVENTS
Oil paints	Turpentine, mineral spirits, benzine, or suitable commercial brush cleaner.
Casein and latex paints	Water.
Shellac	Alcohol.
Lacquer	Lacquer thinner. Use the thinner made by the manufacturer of the lacquer used.

Not only will the bristles of a hog bristle brush become soft, but the handle and wedge of any brush will swell. When the brush dries, the wooden parts will shrink, and the metal ferrule will become loose.

3. Never jab a brush into corners.

4. Never use a nylon bristle brush in lacquer, or in paint and varnish remover. The nylon will soften.

5. Never let paint dry in the bristles of a brush.

HOW TO RESTORE A BRUSH

Often it is possible to restore a brush that looks as if it should be thrown away. By carefully following these steps, an old, hardened brush can be restored and used again.

Steps in Restoring a Brush

1. Soak the brush in a container of paint and varnish remover, or commercial brush cleaner. Soak nylon brushes in a special commercial brush cleaner that will not soften the nylon.

2. With a scraper, or steel comb, remove the softened paint from the outside of the bristles.

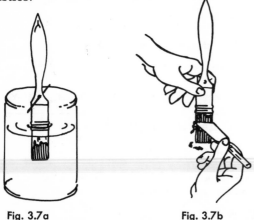

Fig. 3.7a   Fig. 3.7b

3. Wash the brush in turpentine or in mineral spirits to remove hardened oil paints. Use soap and water to remove hardened water paints.

4. Spin out excess solvent.

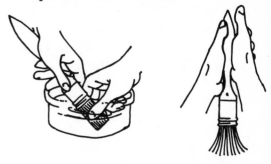

Fig. 3.7c   Fig. 3.7d

5. Wash the brush in a mild solution of soap and water.

6. Rinse the brush in clean water.

Fig. 3.7e   Fig. 3.7f

7. Spin out the excess water.

8. Comb the bristles with a brush comb.

9. Let the brush dry, and wrap it in heavy paper.

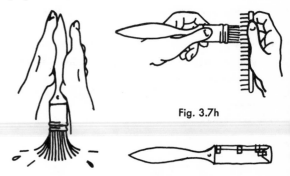

Fig. 3.7g   Fig. 3.7h

Fig. 3.7i

10. If the brush is hog bristle, and is still in good condition, follow the steps for breaking in a new brush.

ROLLING TECHNIQUES

Rollers may be used to apply paint to almost any surface. Surfaces of metal, wood, plaster, and concrete can be painted with rollers. By following a few basic steps, a beginner can do a very professional job.

Steps in Filling a Dip Type Roller

1. Place the paint tray as close as possible to the surface to be painted.

2. Pour enough paint to fill half the sloping bottom of the tray.

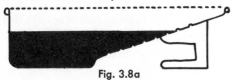

Fig. 3.8a

3. Dip the roller in the paint at a point in the tray where the paint is no deeper than the thickness of the roller cover.

Fig. 3.8b

4. Push the roller back and forth along the rough part of the tray until the roller cover has absorbed as much paint as possible.

Fig. 3.8c

5. Wash the roller tray with the proper thinners at the end of each job. If the trays are washed thoroughly after each job, they will last a long time.

Steps in Applying Paint to Ceilings with Rollers

1. Fill the roller with paint.

2. Paint the ceiling across its narrowest part. Start at one end of the room, and paint a strip as wide as you can reach comfortably.

3. Paint as fast as you can, using a back-and-forth motion of the roller.

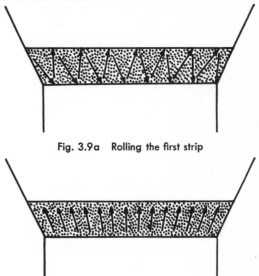

Fig. 3.9a   Rolling the first strip

Fig. 3.9b   Finish rolling the first strip

4. When one width of the ceiling is finished, begin the second strip on the side of the ceiling where the first strip was started.

5. Finish rolling into the area already painted.

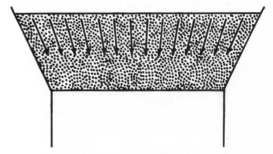

Fig. 3.9c   Finish rolling the second strip

6. Proceed in the same way until the whole ceiling is painted.

Steps in Applying Paint to Walls with Rollers

1. With a loaded roller, start with an upward stroke at one end of the wall. Paint walls in strips no wider than four feet.

2. Without touching either ceiling or baseboard, work the roller up and down the full height of the wall until most of the paint is out of the roller. Do not try to cover the surface completely with one full roller.

3. Return to the starting point and fill in the areas that were not covered. Do not touch ceiling or baseboard.

Fig. 3.10a

4. When one entire wall is covered with paint, roll across the top of the wall as close as possible to the ceiling. Do not allow the roller to touch the ceiling.

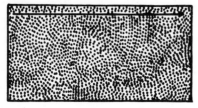

Fig. 3.10b

5. At one end of the wall, roll up to the ceiling. Lift the roller at the end of the stroke and roll down to the baseboard. Overlap each stroke by at least 50%.

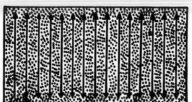

Fig. 3.10c

6. Roll across the bottom of the wall, painting as close as possible to the baseboard without getting paint on the baseboard.

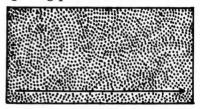

Fig. 3.10d

7. Repeat the operation for each wall.

Points to Remember About Painting with Rollers

1. When painting walls, start painting as close as possible to a corner without getting paint on the other wall.

2. Lift the roller at the end of each stroke.

3. Overlap the previous stroke by at least 50%.

4. Work at a comfortable pace. Keep a wet edge at all times.

5. Finish rolling into the area already painted to prevent lap marks from showing.

6. Use a brush to paint in corners, and around windows, doors, and baseboards. Also, use a brush to make a straight line along the top of the wall when the wall is a different colour from the ceiling.

7. Do not return to touch up the wall with the roller after the paint has had time to set.

Steps in Cleaning a Roller

1. Scrape excess paint off the roller with a putty knife or scraper.

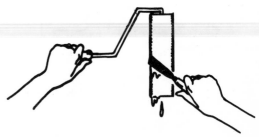

Fig. 3.11a

2. Remove the sleeve from the handle.

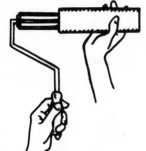

Fig. 3.11b

3. Wash the sleeve in the proper thinner.

Fig. 3.11c

4. Put the sleeve on the handle and spin out the excess thinner.

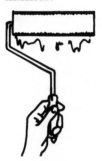

Fig. 3.11d

SPRAY GUN TECHNIQUES

Using a spray gun is fairly easy. However, it is wise to practise spraying an old cardboard box to get the feel of spraying. Ten or fifteen minutes of practice will give you the feel of the gun. If it is possible, try a few simple jobs before you try anything difficult.

Spraying Even Coats of Finish

It is most important that the surface being sprayed receives an even coat. There are several points to keep in mind to ensure that the coat of finish is even.

1. Keep the spray gun the same distance from the work at all times. The correct distance is about 8″. Keep your wrist loose. If you keep your wrist stiff, the gun will arc. Arcing means that the gun is too close to the work at the centre, and is too far from the work at the edges.

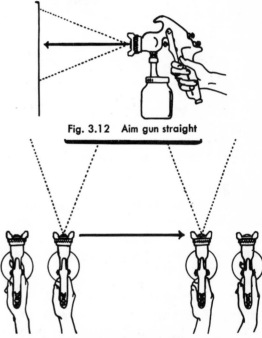

Fig. 3.12 Aim gun straight

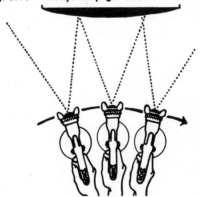

Fig. 3.13 Always keep gun same distance from work

Fig. 3.14 Arcing

2. Overlap each stroke by 50%. Each stroke consists of a spray that is heavy at the centre, and light at the edges of the spray. The light edge of the spray is called the overspray. To overlap the previous stroke, aim the gun at the bottom of the previous stroke.

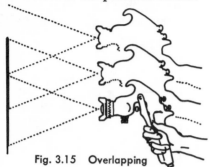

Fig. 3.15   Overlapping

3. Move the gun at a constant speed. The movement of the gun is known as stroking.

4. Release the trigger at the end of each stroke.

5. Do not spray too large an area at once. If you do, you will have to swing your arm too much, or move your feet to cover the entire width of the area being sprayed. The result will be an uneven coat.

Spraying Various Surfaces

Remember that when you are spraying, not all the paint will land on the surface being sprayed. If you are not spraying in a special booth, always put the object being sprayed on paper so that floors are not sprayed. To protect walls, put some protective covering between the object and the wall. If you are spraying a part of a wall or part of some other surface, mask the rest of the surface. Masking is done by taping paper on the part of the surface that is not to be sprayed. There is a special tape known as masking tape for doing this job.

1. Small panels must be sprayed with a horizontal stroke. Before starting the horizontal stroke, the panel should be banded. Banding consists of spraying a vertical stroke at each end of the panel. If you don't band the panel, there will not be enough paint on the ends of the panel. Banding also saves paint by reducing the amount of overspray that is sprayed past the panel.

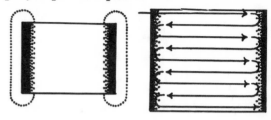

Fig. 3.16a   Banding   Fig. 3.16b   Spraying small panels

2. Large panels can be treated in two ways. They can be treated like a series of small panels. The large panel is divided into a number of small panels, each of which is painted separately. Large panels can also be sprayed vertically. Either of these methods can be used to achieve an even coat of finish.

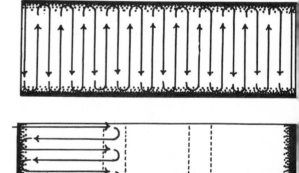

Fig. 3.16c   Two ways to spray large panels

3. Circular panels are painted like small panels. First, an area of banding is sprayed around the rim of the circle. Then, the panel is sprayed horizontally.

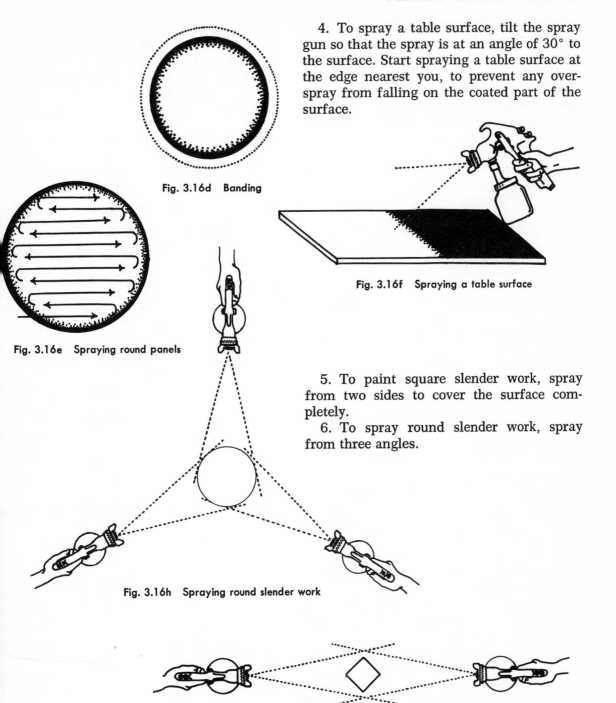

4. To spray a table surface, tilt the spray gun so that the spray is at an angle of 30° to the surface. Start spraying a table surface at the edge nearest you, to prevent any overspray from falling on the coated part of the surface.

Fig. 3.16d   Banding

Fig. 3.16f   Spraying a table surface

Fig. 3.16e   Spraying round panels

5. To paint square slender work, spray from two sides to cover the surface completely.

6. To spray round slender work, spray from three angles.

Fig. 3.16h   Spraying round slender work

Fig. 3.16g   Spraying square slender work

7. The outside corners of pieces such as kitchen cupboards are sprayed straight on. The uneven coating that results will be corrected when the rest of the outside of the cupboard is sprayed. Inside corners are sprayed from two directions. First, the spray is aimed at one side of the inside of the piece as close to the corner as possible. Then, the other side that forms the corner is sprayed. The overspray will get into the corner, and will ensure an even coat.

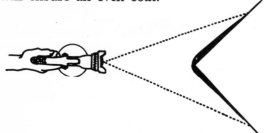

Fig. 3.16i   Spraying outside corners

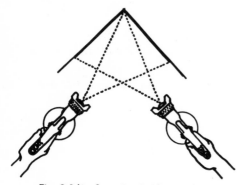

Fig. 3.16j   Spraying inside corners

Points to Remember When Spraying

1. Never spray where the spray or fumes can reach a flame.

2. Always try to spray in a ventilated area.

3. Always wear a gauze mask when you are spraying.

4. Use the correct pressure for the type of gun you are using, and the material you are spraying. When you are using a suction feed gun, spray stains with a pressure of about 25 pounds and heavier paint with 40-50 pounds of pressure. When you are using a pressure feed gun with a cup, never use over 40 pounds of pressure, unless the paint supply is kept in a tank, when somewhat greater pressure can be used. As with suction feed guns, use only 25 pounds of pressure for stains.

HOW TO CLEAN A SPRAY GUN

Cleaning a spray gun properly, immediately after the job is finished, will save the painter a great deal of time and trouble the next time he has to use the equipment.

Steps in Cleaning a Spray Gun

1. Pour out any paint that is left in the cup or container.

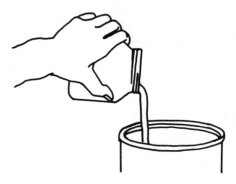

Fig. 3.17a

2. Rinse the cup with the proper solvent.

Fig. 3.17b

3. Wipe out any excess solvent with a rag.

Fig. 3.17c

4. Half-fill the cup with solvent.
5. Spray out the solvent.

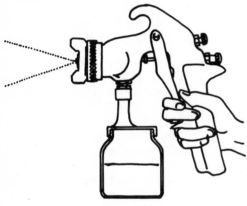

Fig. 3.17d

6. Remove the nozzle and fluid needle.
7. Rinse the nozzle and fluid needle in solvent. Wipe them dry.

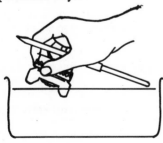

Fig. 3.17e

8. Replace all parts.

9. Wipe the paint off the exterior of the gun and cup.

Fig. 3.17f

10. Oil around the fluid needle packing nut and the air valve packing nut.

Fig. 3.17g

Points to Remember About Cleaning a Spray Gun

1. Never put the entire gun into the solvent. Solvent will dry the packing around the fluid needle and air valve. If this packing dries, paint will leak.

2. Never use a piece of wire to clean out holes in the air cap, or in any other part of the gun. Use a toothpick or broom bristle to clean holes. A piece of wire may enlarge the holes and allow too much paint to pass through them.

THE MOST COMMON SPRAYING FAULTS AND THEIR REMEDIES

FAULT	CAUSE	REMEDY
Sags or runs	1. Dirty air cap and fluid tip.	1. Remove cap and fluid tip, and clean with lacquer thinners.
	2. Gun held too close to surface.	2. Hold gun about 8″ away from surface.
	3. Trigger not released at end of each stroke.	3. Release trigger at end of each stroke.
	4. Material thinned too much.	4. When mixing material, add correct amount of solvent.
	5. Moving gun across the surface too slowly.	5. Move gun a little more quickly.
Streaks	1. Not overlapping strokes correctly or enough.	1. Overlap previous stroke by 50%.
	2. Gun held at wrong angle to surface.	2. Hold gun at a 90° angle to surface at all times.
	3. Split spray.	3. Reduce air or change air cap.
Orange peel	1. Material not thinned enough.	1. Add correct amount of thinner.
	2. Gun not spraying a wet enough coat.	2. Move gun slowly enough to give a wet coat but quickly enough to prevent runs.
	3. Using wrong air cap.	3. Choose correct air cap for the material being sprayed.
	4. Drafts of air passing over wet paint.	4. Eliminate drafts if possible.
	5. Wrong thinner used in material.	5. Use thinner recommended by manufacturer.
	6. Gun too far from or too close to the surface.	6. Hold gun 8″ from the surface.
Too much spray fog	1. Air pressure too high.	1. Adjust air pressure.
	2. Gun held too far from surface.	2. Hold gun 8″ from the surface.
	3. Material too thin.	3. Use correct amount of thinner.
	4. Spraying too much past edge of object.	4. Release trigger just as gun passes edge of object.
Gun will not spray	1. Out of paint.	1. Add paint.
	2. Piece of grit, dirt, skin, or paint blocking air cap or fluid tip.	2. Remove air cap and fluid tip. Clean in lacquer thinners. Strain paint before spraying.
	3. Wrong air cap.	3. Replace with correct air cap.
Spray gun leaks	1. Fluid needle packing nut too tight.	1. Loosen nut.
	2. Fluid needle packing is dry.	2. Oil packing and fluid needle.
	3. Damaged fluid needle tip.	3. Replace fluid needle.

Paint sputters when coming out of gun	1. Fluid tip not tightened properly.	1. Replace gasket and tighten tip firmly.
	2. Not enough paint in the gun.	2. Refill cup.
	3. Fluid passageway obstructed.	3. Remove fluid needle, tip, and tube. Clean thoroughly and replace these parts.
	4. Paint is too heavy for a suction feed gun.	4. Thin paint properly before spraying.
	5. Clogged air vent on suction feed gun.	5. Clean air vent.

If the spray gun is cleaned properly and thoroughly after each use, most spraying problems will be eliminated. Always strain the paint before spraying, no matter how clean the paint seems. Bits of dirt can get into the paint when it is being stirred.

Never use a metal object, such as a wire or nail, to clean any openings in the spray gun. These openings are precision machined and wire or nails can damage the openings, causing the spray pattern to be distorted.

ASSIGNMENT

1. What are the steps in pre-conditioning a hog bristle brush?
2. Why should hog bristle brushes be pre-conditioned?
3. Why are nylon bristle brushes not pre-conditioned?
4. What kind of brush is used to apply primers?
5. How are primers applied to a surface?
6. What happens if oil paints are applied when the temperature is above 80°F.?
7. How are water paints applied to a surface?
8. What are the steps in brushing paint?
9. What happens if wet paint overlaps dry paint?
10. When you are using water paints, how can you help keep the brush marks from showing?
11. How do you clean a brush that has been used in latex paint?
12. What happens if a brush is soaked in water?
13. How is a dip type roller filled with paint?
14. What are the steps for painting a ceiling with a roller?
15. How do you clean a roller that has been used in oil paint? What solvent do you use?
16. How far from a surface should you hold a spray gun when you are spraying?
17. How do you make sure that you spray only what you want to spray?
18. What is the purpose of banding?
19. Draw a diagram to show how to spray round, slender work.
20. What are the steps in cleaning a spray gun?

4 PAINT

WORDS TO LEARN

Anti-Foam Agents — chemicals added to casein and latex paints to prevent suds forming

Anti-Skin Agents — chemicals added to paint to prevent a skin from forming on the surface of the paint when paint is left standing in the can

Pigment — the solid part of paint

Plasticizers — material added to lacquer to increase the lacquer's toughness

Resin — a vehicle made from the gum of a tree

Rosin — a pigment made from the gum of a tree

Vehicle — the liquid part of paint

Flat — unshiny

High-Gloss — shiny

Opaque — cannot be seen through

Synthetic — man-made

Transparent — can be seen through

BASIC FACTS ABOUT PAINT

Before a person can do a good job in any field, he must know something about the product he uses. What is it? How is it made? What does it do?

Paint is a semi-liquid made of a pigment in a vehicle. It is applied to a surface to provide that surface with a protective, decorative coating. It can be applied to a surface with a brush, with a roller, or with a spray gun. An object can also be painted by dipping it in paint.

Paint can be opaque, or transparent. Opaque paint completely hides the surface being painted. Transparent paint is clear, like glass. Paint can also be semi-transparent, like stain, which hides only a little of the surface that is covered.

Fig. 4.1a   Opaque paint

Fig. 4.1b   Transparent paint

24

There are high-gloss paints that dry with a high shine. Some paints are low-gloss, which means that they dry with a slightly shiny finish. Other paints are flat-finish, which means that they dry with no shine at all.

WHAT IS IN PAINT

Basically, paint is made of two things – pigment and vehicle. There are several types of each. A pigment is the part of the paint that colours or hides the surface being painted. A vehicle is the liquid part of the paint.

Pigments

1. Prime pigment is either white or coloured powder, or a combination of both.

2. Extender is a powder that hides very little or none of the surface. An extender is used to help the flow of the paint. Extenders also help to reduce the price of paint.

Vehicles

The vehicle of a paint keeps the pigment from separating, makes the paint stick to the surface, and gives the paint its protective powers. There are four general classifications of liquids used as vehicles:

1. Solvents are vehicles that hold pigments in solution. Turpentine, alcohol, and water are the most common solvents used in paint.

2. Oil vehicles hold pigments in suspension. Both animal and vegetable oils are used as vehicles.

3. Resins are vehicles that hold pigments in suspension. Most of the resins used in making paint are synthetic.

4. Additives are used in paint as driers, perfumes, plasticizers, anti-skin agents, and anti-foam agents.

WHAT PAINT DOES

1. Paint preserves a surface. Wood will rot or dry out, and metal will rust very quickly, if not protected by some kind of coating.

2. Paint adds beauty to homes, offices, and places of work, or study.

3. Paint helps to keep our surroundings bright and sanitary. Painted surfaces are easy to clean, and resist moisture.

4. Paint increases the value of property. A coat or two of paint improves old buildings and adds to their asking price.

5. Paint can absorb light or reflect it. In study rooms, hospitals, offices, and homes the correct use of paint helps to achieve proper lighting.

Paint does many more things. See how many you can discover.

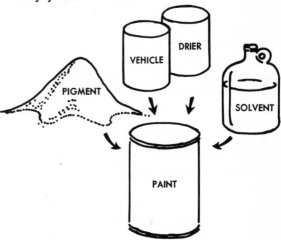

Fig. 4.2 What is in paint

KINDS OF PAINT

Paints can be divided into two types. One type contains coloured pigment, the other colourless pigment.

Colour-Pigmented Paints

1. Oil paints consist of a pigment suspended in oil. Oil paints require special thinners, such as turpentine or mineral spirits, to help the paint to spread easily. Enamels, semi-gloss paints, flat oil paints, undercoats,

and primers are examples of oil paints.

2. Alkyd paints have a vehicle made partly of vegetable oil. The rest of the vehicle is synthetic. Mineral spirits, odourless thinners, or turpentine are used to thin alkyds. Alkyds, are very tough and resistant to scrubbing, and are very easy to apply. Alkyd paints have much less odour than regular oil paints.

3. Latex paints have synthetic vehicles made from some of the same things that are used to make plastics. For this reason they are sometimes called plastic paints. Latex paints have little or no odour and are quick-drying. A second coat of paint can usually be applied within an hour after the first coat has been applied. Latex paints need no special solvents for thinning; all that is needed is water. Brushes and rollers are cleaned very easily by running water from a tap over them. Some latex paints can be used both outside and inside. Others can be used outside only, because they dry too slowly and wrinkle inside.

4. Casein paints have a vehicle made of milk mixed with an acid. Casein paints dry very quickly, and can be recoated within an hour after the application of the first coat. They will usually cover a light surface in one coat; a dark surface may require two coats. Like latex paints, casein paints are thinned with water. Unlike latex paints, casein paints cannot be used outside.

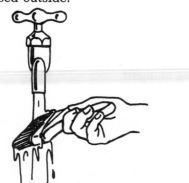

Fig. 4.3   Cleaning a brush used in water paint

5. Colours-in-oil are highly pigmented oil paints that are used only to tint oil paints. They are never used alone because they do not dry. In the past, when painters often mixed their own colours, these paints were widely used. Today the painter does not use them often because he can usually buy the colour he wants already mixed.

Colourless-Pigmented Paints

1. Varnishes are colourless rosins dissolved in thinners. Thus, a varnish finish is clear instead of opaque. There are five different types of varnish.

(a) Oleoresinous varnishes are the most common ones used. They are made from rosin, oil, and drier with a fast-evaporating liquid that serves as a thinner. Rubbing varnish, spar varnish, floor varnish, and furniture varnish are all oleoresinous varnishes.

(b) Natural varnish, known as oriental Japanese, or Chinese lacquer, is made from the fluids of trees that grow in the far east.

(c) Catalytic varnishes have an agent added to them to help them dry.

(d) Water varnishes are used to protect artwork.

(e) Spirit varnish is made from rosin mixed with a fast-evaporating liquid. When the liquid evaporates, the rosin remains as a film on the surface that has been covered. This type of varnish is used on playing cards, food cartons, and hulls of boats.

2. Shellac takes its name from the lac insect that makes the raw material for this useful, transparent coating. The lac insect secretes a resinous material called lac. The lac is removed from the trees where the insect lives, is placed in cloth bags, heated until it becomes a liquid, and then strained. The strained liquid is poured onto a flat surface to dry into a thin sheet. When the sheet hardens, it is broken into flakes. The flakes are dissolved in alcohol. The solution is called

orange shellac. White shellac is orange shellac that has been bleached.

3. Lacquer is made from shellac flakes and a fast-drying thinner. Lacquer gives a tough, long-wearing finish that is easy to sand, rub, or patch. Because lacquer dries very quickly, the best way to apply it is by spray gun.

ASSIGNMENT

1. What is paint?
2. What are three things that paint does?
3. What is the difference between opaque and transparent paints?
4. Name three types of paint that have coloured pigments.
5. Name two types of paint that have colourless pigments.
6. What is a vehicle in paint?
7. List three advantages of latex paints.
8. What is the most common type of varnish?
9. What is orange shellac?
10. Why should lacquers be applied with a spray gun?

5 PIGMENTS, OILS, RESINS AND THINNERS

WORDS TO LEARN

Colour Retention — the ability of a material to keep its colour

Elasticity — the ability of a material to stretch and come back to shape; an important feature of exterior paints

Prime Pigment — the basic, white pigment in paint

Durable — able to last

Bind — hold together

Chalking — a paint surface turning to powder; a good feature of exterior paints

Penetrate — soak into

PIGMENTS

There are three types of pigments. The following are examples of each type.

Prime Pigments

1. Titanium dioxide, the most important of the white pigments, is the whitest of pigments, and therefore has the best hiding qualities. It is also the most expensive prime pigment. Titanium dioxide is used in both exterior paints and interior paints.

2. White lead, the oldest known prime pigment, is very good for exterior paint. The durability and gradual chalking of white lead paints are both good features of an exterior paint.

3. Zinc oxide, is a very hard white pigment, with none of the elasticity required in all paints. It is therefore, always used with another pigment. Zinc oxide helps the paint surface to wear longer, adds to the paint's colour retention, helps to prevent mildew from forming on exterior surfaces, and helps to prevent lead from chalking too fast.

Coloured Pigments

Coloured pigments are divided into four classes, depending upon the source.

1. Earth, or mineral, colours are prepared from natural earths. The minerals must be purified, but they are not treated with chemicals. Ochre, umber, sienna, and venetian red are some of the coloured earth pigments.

2. Vegetable colours are made from chemically treated vegetable material. Brunswick black, for example, is made from vine twigs, grape husks, or cocoanut shells. Vandyke brown comes from decayed vegetation.

3. Animal colours are obtained from a variety of animals and animal products. The best known animal colour is carmine, which is obtained from an insect. Ivory black, coach black, and drop black are made by charring bones and then grinding them into a fine powder.

4. Chemical colours, made by chemical processes, are divided into two classes. True pigments are chrome yellows, prussian, cobalt, and ultramarine blues, some of the bright reds, and chrome greens. Lakes are the second type of chemical colours. They are dyes made from coal tar. Crimson, madder, rose, scarlet, and mauve are some of the lake colours. Chemical colours fade very quickly if they are exposed to strong light.

Carbon black and lamp black are two chemical colours made from the soot of burnt gas and oil. These blacks are not as pure as the animal blacks.

Extenders

Extender pigments have very little or no hiding power. They help paint to flow more easily and lower the paint's gloss.

1. China clay is an extender that enables paint to be brushed easily. This extender is used a great deal in water-thinned paints.

2. Talc, a very popular extender pigment, is used to make paint smooth, and it helps prevent other pigments from settling and caking. Talc is used most often in interior flat-finish paints.

3. Silica, made from quartz rock, is an extender pigment used to make fillers for open-grained woods. Silica is also used to lower the gloss of varnish. If the dust of silica is inhaled over a long period of time, it can damage the lungs.

VEHICLES

Oil

Oil vehicles bind pigments and hold the pigment to the surface being painted.

1. Linseed oil, which is obtained from the seeds of the flax plant, is the best oil vehicle for binding pigments and holding them to the surface being painted. There are two types of linseed oil. The raw oil is used in exterior paints. The boiled oil is used in gloss paints.

2. Soybean oil, made from the soybean, makes a paint that brushes very easily. Paints with a soybean oil vehicle have good colour retention, which makes such paints well suited for use in non-yellowing enamels. Soybean oil is usually mixed with other oils to help speed the drying of the paint.

3. Tung oil, made from the seeds of the fruit of the tung tree, is used in spar varnishes, concrete paints, marine finishes, and four-hour enamels. Tung oil vehicle paints may be used for all interior and exterior jobs where fast drying and durability are needed.

4. Fish oil, also known as menhaden oil, is made from menhaden fish. Fish oil is the only animal oil used in making paint. Paints with fish oil vehicles are very heat resistant. For smoke stacks, boiler parts, and engine parts, fish oil paints are ideal.

Resin

Resins are an important part of paints, varnishes, and lacquers. Resins speed drying, improve resistance to chemicals, add to gloss and gloss retention, and help paint to stick to a surface. There are both natural and synthetic resins. Copal, dammar, and shellac are natural resins. Ester gum, copal ester, alkyds, vinyl, and acrylic are synthetic resins. The resins used in most modern paints are synthetic.

Thinners

Thinners help speed the drying of paint and help the paint penetrate the surface being painted. They must be carefully selected. A thinner that is very good for one paint may be bad for another paint. As new kinds of paints are manufactured, new thinners must be produced for them. Before thinning any paint, be sure to read the label on the paint can and follow the instructions of the manufacturer.

1. Gum spirits are made from the sap of living pine trees. The sap is collected and refined into pure spirits of turpentine. This type of turpentine is used only to thin enamels and quick-drying varnishes. It is too costly to use for washing brushes or rollers. Gum spirits evaporate very quickly and do not destroy any property of the paint.

2. Wood turpentine is made by boiling the wood of pine tree stumps, cooling the steam, and collecting the liquid in a container. This type of turpentine is cheaper than gum spirits and is therefore used for thinning oil paint, and washing any tools used in an oil paint.

3. Mineral spirits, made from petroleum, are much cheaper than turpentine, but they are not as effective.

4. Alcohol is used to thin shellac. It is also used to wash off any grease that may be on a surface that is to be painted. There are two types of alcohol used in painting. Grain alcohol is made from oats, wheat, or other grain. Although it is not naturally poisonous, some of the substances that are added to it before it is sold *are* poisonous. When it has been treated for sale, it is called denatured alcohol. The other type of alcohol is made from wood. Wood alcohol is naturally poisonous.

5. Benzol, made from coal tar, is used to make paint and varnish remover.

Remember: No one thinner can be used with all types of oil paints. Turpentine works with some oil paints; mineral spirits work with others. If you have never used a certain type of paint, find out which thinners you can use with it before you use the paint.

ASSIGNMENT

1. Name three types of pigments.
2. Name the four classes of coloured pigments. Name one example of each class.
3. What does an extender do?
4. Name three extenders.
5. Name three oils that are used as vehicles in paint.
6. What kind of linseed oil is used for exterior paint?
7. Name a vehicle that helps paint keep its colour.
8. What are resins used for in paint?
9. Name three types of thinners. For what is each one used?

6 SANDING

Sanding is the most important step in preparing a wood surface for a finish. Sanding removes tool marks and smoothes the surface so that the finishing materials will bring out the beauty of the wood. Take time to do the sanding properly, and you will produce a professional looking job.

Sanding can be done by hand or by a variety of power tools. Disc and belt sanders are good for rough sanding. Vibrating type sanders are excellent for sanding between coats of a finish. Although power tools save a lot of time, the final sanding should be done by hand.

Courtesy Skil Corporation (Canada) Ltd.

Fig. 6.1   Belt sander

Courtesy Skil Corporation (Canada) Ltd.

Fig. 6.2   Vibrating sander

When you are sanding by hand, use some backing, other than the fingers, for the sandpaper. Various types of sanding blocks are available for backing sandpaper. A board to which has been tacked a layer of foam rubber makes an excellent sanding block. Unpadded blocks should not be used. If a piece of sawdust or grit gets between the sandpaper and the unpadded block, there is a danger that the wood will be scratched.

Steps in Sanding New Wood for Painting and Staining

1. Begin sanding new wood with coarse sandpaper. Always sand bare wood with the grain to remove any ridges and glue stains. The coarse paper will leave scratches over the entire surface.

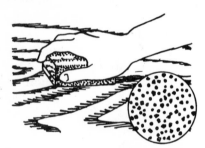

Fig. 6.3a   Sanding with coarse sandpaper

2. Sand with medium sandpaper. Sand in the direction of the grain of the wood. Sand until the scratches made by the coarse sandpaper have been eliminated.

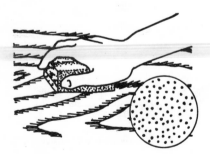

Fig. 6.3b   Sanding with medium sandpaper

3. Sand with a fine sandpaper, again with the grain of the wood.

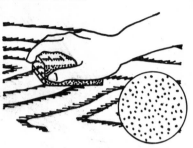

Fig. 6.3c   Sanding with fine sandpaper

4. For the final sanding, use a very fine sandpaper. Some decorators apply a wash coat of shellac before the final sanding; other decorators dampen the wood with water. Either of these methods will raise the grain of the wood. When the wood is dry, and the raised grain is sanded, a very smooth wood surface is produced.

Fig. 6.3d   Raising the grain

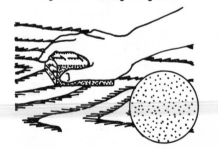

Fig. 6.3e   Sanding with very fine sandpaper

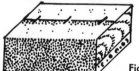

Fig. 6.4   Sanding block

Points to Remember About Sanding

1. Always apply an even pressure from the beginning to the end of the stroke.

2. Do not allow the sanding block to extend more than a quarter of its length beyond the edge of the surface, for if you do, you will round the edge.

3. Do not use steel wool on bare wood; it will blacken the wood. Very fine steel wool may, however, be used between coats of wood finish.

4. Never sand across the grain of bare wood. Cross-grain sanding makes scratches that are nearly impossible to remove. Such scratches may not be visable until a stain or varnish coat has been applied to the surface. When such coats are applied the scratches may become very obvious.

5. Sand veneers very carefully with medium and fine sandpapers. Rough sandpaper may cut through the veneer to the core stock.

SANDING PAINTED WOOD

Sandpaper is used both for preparing surfaces for painting, and for smoothing undercoats, enamels, and varnishes to make them ready for finishing coats. Often, new wood is given a prime coat before it is sanded, especially if the wood is for casings, doors, baseboards, and cupboards in a new house. When the prime coat is dry, the wood is sanded as if it were old wood with a painted surface.

Steps in Sanding Painted Wood

1. Use a medium or fine sandpaper to smooth flat painted surfaces. Do not scratch through the paint to the bare wood. Such scratches will show in the following coats of paint.

2. Sand with the grain of the wood wherever possible; otherwise, sand with the longest stroke.

3. Use #2 or #3 steel wool for smoothing mouldings or irregular surfaces. Unravel one pad of steel wool and wrap it around a second pad.

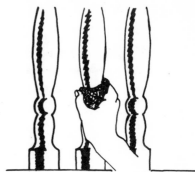

Fig. 6.5

4. Some curved surfaces may need sanding with sandpaper to remove roughness. Wrap a piece of sandpaper around a pointed stick to get at these places.

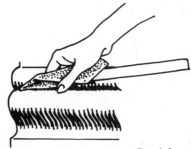

Fig. 6.6

ASSIGNMENT

1. Why must a surface be sanded before it is painted?
2. Draw a diagram of a sanding block.
3. Why are sanding blocks padded?
4. What are the steps in sanding a new wood surface?
5. What happens when a wash coat of shellac is applied before the final sanding?
6. What happens if bare wood is sanded with steel wool?
7. Why should bare wood never be sanded across the grain?

7 PAINTING A NEW WOOD SURFACE

WORDS TO LEARN

Eggshell Enamel — a paint that has very little shine

Primer — the first coat of paint applied to any surface

Undercoat — the coat of paint applied just before the finish coat

Flashy Finish — a painted surface that has dull and shiny spots

Inadequate — not good enough

Lustre — shine

Low Lustre — almost no shine

The most important step in finishing new wood is the proper preparation of the surface to be painted. Paint must be applied over a well prepared surface to achieve worthwhile results.

Most unsatisfactory paint jobs are due to one or more of the following faults:

1. improperly prepared surface,
2. inadequate undercoat,
3. using the wrong paint, or
4. improperly applied paint.

Modern paints are made to very high technical standards. If the paint manufacturer's instructions are not followed, the paint will not do the job for which it is intended. It is important, therefore, that the painter follow the directions printed on the labels of paint cans. Also, he must follow the basic rules for applying all types of paint.

PAINTING NEW WOOD

The first coat of paint on new wood, whether it is inside or outside a building, is the most important coat. The first coat can be compared to the foundation of a house. The stronger the foundation, the longer the house will last. The stronger the first coat of paint is, the longer the paint job will last.

PRIME COAT

Many paint jobs are ruined because the wrong primer or first coat is used and applied over an improperly prepared surface. New wood primers made for interior use must not be used for exterior new wood. Exterior primers contain more oil for every hundred pounds of rosin used than interior primers do. For this reason, exterior primers are called long oil primers. The oil gives the paint the ability to stretch or contract. Because outside temperatures change so much, the paint must be able to stretch and contract to prevent cracking. Because interior temperatures are fairly constant, interior primers need not be so elastic.

If the surface of the wood is very rough, it should be sanded before the prime coat is applied. Otherwise, no sanding is needed.

TOOLS	MATERIALS
Push broom	Shellac
Dust brush	Alcohol or benzine
Putty knife	Thinners
Scraper	Paint
Drop sheets or paper	
Ladders	
Pots	
Brushes	
Rags	

Steps in Applying a Prime Coat

1. Clean out the working area.

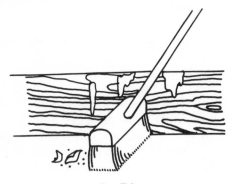

Fig. 7.1a

2. Clean any mortar splashes or plaster off the wood.

Fig. 7.1b

3. Wash off any grease, tar, or oil marks with alcohol or benzine.

Fig. 7.1c

4. Dust any dust or loose dirt off the surface to be painted.

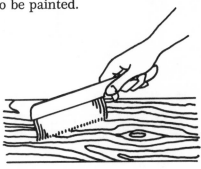

Fig. 7.1d

5. Shellac all tar marks, resinous spots, and knots.

Fig. 7.1e

6. Prepare the paint and brushes.

Fig. 7.1f

7. Cover the floor with drop sheets or paper.

8. Put ladders in place.

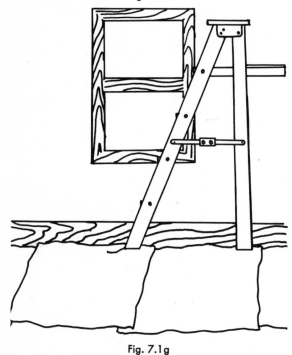

Fig. 7.1g

9. Apply the primer.

Fig. 7.1h

Points to Remember About Applying the Prime Coat

1. Be as careful when you are applying the prime coat as when you are applying the finish coat. New wood primer not only seals the pores of the wood, but it also provides a base for following coats of paint.

2. Never putty nail holes or cracks in the wood before the prime coat has been applied. Primer seals the wood, preventing the oil in the putty from soaking into the wood. If the oil of the putty soaks into the wood, the putty will dry, leaving only a dry powder that will fall out in time.

3. Use the best wood primer that is available.

4. Brush the primer *into* the wood so that it will not peel. Finish brushing with the grain of the wood.

5. Prepare both interior and exterior woodwork for painting in the same way. Follow the steps in sanding new wood. Use exterior primer for exterior surfaces. Use interior primer for interior surfaces.

6. Have sufficient primer available for the job. Most new wood primers will cover up to 600 square feet per gallon of primer.

UNDERCOAT

The second coat of paint on new wood is called the undercoat because it is the coat of paint under the finish coat. It is sometimes called the putty coat because all puttying of nail holes and cracks is done before the undercoat is applied.

Undercoats should have excellent hiding powers, and dry to a smooth, hard finish. Undercoats must show no brush marks, must hold their colour well, and must form a good "tooth" for following coats of paint. Undercoats should be approximately the same colour as the finish coat.

TOOLS	MATERIALS
Sandpaper	Putty
Steel wool	Colour-in-oil
Putty knife	Thinners
Drop sheets	Paint
Duster	
Paint pots	
Brushes	
Rags	

Steps in Applying the Undercoat

1. Smooth all the primed wood with sandpaper or steel wool. Use medium sandpaper for flat surfaces. Use #3 steel wool for mouldings and curved surfaces. Always sand with the grain of the wood.

Fig. 7.2a

2. Dust off all traces of steel wool and dirt.

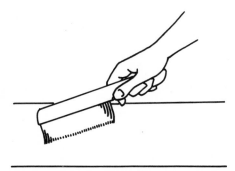

Fig. 7.2b

3. Putty all nail holes and cracks. Fill the nail holes so that the putty is slightly above the surface of the wood. If the putty is applied level with the surface of the wood, the shrinking of the putty as it dries will leave a slight depression. The paint will not hide this depression.

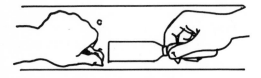

Fig. 7.2c

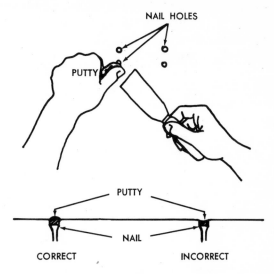

NAIL HOLES

PUTTY

PUTTY

NAIL

CORRECT   INCORRECT

Fig. 7.2d

4. Clean out the working area.
5. Put ladders and drop sheets in place.

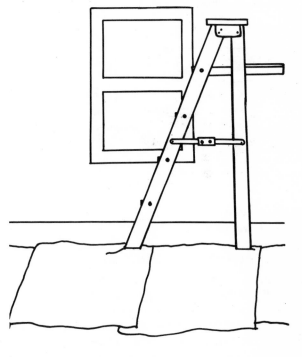

Fig. 7.2e

6. Prepare the undercoat. If the finish coat is to be a colour other than white, tint the undercoat with colour-in oil to approximately the same colour as the finish coat.

Fig. 7.2f

7. Apply the undercoat carefully, so that it lies evenly on the surface. Do *not* try to brush it *into* the wood.

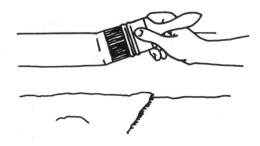

Fig. 7.2g

Points to Remember About Applying the Undercoat

1. Never use flat-finish paint as an undercoat. Flat-finish paint does not dry hard and smooth enough to act as an undercoat.

2. If the undercoat is not applied properly, the finish coat will be "flashy". A flashy finish is one that has an uneven shine.

3. Enamel undercoats will cover up to 600 square feet per gallon.

FINISH COAT

A great many types of paint are available for finish coats. The type selected will depend upon the type of finish desired. In kitchens and bathrooms, where considerable washing is done, use high-gloss or semi-gloss enamel. In bedrooms, hallways, living rooms, and dining rooms, eggshell enamel is very decorative.

TOOLS	MATERIALS
Sandpaper	Putty
Putty knife	Thinners
Drop sheets	Paint
Duster	
Paint pots	
Brushes	

Steps in Applying the Finish Coat

1. Sand the undercoated surface with fine sandpaper. If the prime coat was sanded properly, the undercoat will need very little sanding.

2. Dust off all traces of dirt.

3. Putty any nail holes and cracks that have been missed. Allow the putty to dry.

4. Sweep the floor.

5. Put drop sheets or paper in place. Set up the ladders.

6. Prepare the paint and brushes.

7. Apply the paint.

Points to Remember About Applying the Finish Coat

1. For a low lustre finish, use eggshell finish enamel.

2. Brush a finish coat as little as possible.

3. Prime coats are brushed into the surface of the wood. Undercoats and finish coats lie on the surface.

4. Finish coats cover approximately 700 square feet per gallon of paint.

Fig. 7.3   Use a wide brush to paint wide surfaces

Fig. 7.4   Use a narrow brush to paint narrow surfaces

ASSIGNMENT

1. What is the most important coat of paint on any surface? Why?

2. Why are exterior oil primers called long oil primers?

3. What are the steps in applying a prime coat?

4. How many gallons of primer are needed to cover 1,800 square feet?

5. What is another name for an undercoat?

6. Draw a diagram to show how to putty holes properly.

7. Why should you not use a flat-finish paint as an undercoat?

8. How many square feet will one quart of undercoat cover?

9. What kind of finish coat should be used in a kitchen?

10. How many pints of a finish paint are needed to cover 700 square feet?

8 REPAINTING WOOD SURFACES

WORDS TO LEARN

Alligatoring — paint film cracking in large pieces

Fig. 8.1a

Blistering — bubbles forming on a painted or varnished surface

Fig. 8.1b

Checking — short, fine cracks on a painted or varnished surface

Fig. 8.1c

Cracking — cracks caused by a finish coat drying before the undercoat is dry

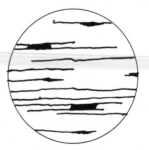

Fig. 8.1d

Orange Peel — the surface of paint or varnish that has dried too fast after spraying

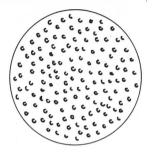

Fig. 8.1e

Peeling — paint coming away from a surface in large pieces

Fig. 8.1f

Wrinkling — paint forming a skin before the paint dries completely through its full thickness

Fig. 8.1g

REPAINTING INTERIOR WOODWORK

Painted woodwork should be washed and sanded before new paint is applied. Paint that is applied over grease and dirt will not dry properly. Improperly dried paint has a tendency to chip. If the old paint is in good condition, and nearly the same colour as the new paint, one finish coat may be all that is needed. If the colour of the new finish coat is very different from the old paint, two coats will be needed; one undercoat, and one finish coat.

If the old paint is cracked, it should be removed to the bare wood. The bare wood is then treated as if it were new wood. Paint can be removed by sanding, with paint and varnish remover, or by burning. Burning is recommended only for exterior woodwork.

TOOLS	MATERIALS
Sponges	Soap and water
Sandpaper	Putty
Putty knife	Paint and varnish
Drop sheets	remover
Duster	Paint
Ladders	
Paint pots	
Brushes	
Rags	

Steps in Preparing and Repainting Interior Woodwork

1. Remove as much furniture as possible from the room. Push the rest of the furniture into the middle of the room, and cover it with drop sheets or paper.

2. Remove all hardware from the surfaces that are to be painted.

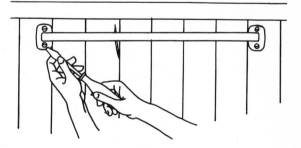

Fig. 8.2a

3. Wash the woodwork with soap and water. Rinse with clear water. Allow to dry.

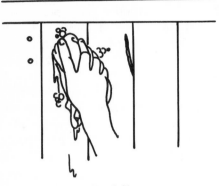

Fig. 8.2b

4. Sand the woodwork with fine sandpaper to remove any gloss from the old paint.

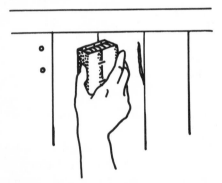

Fig. 8.2c

5. Putty all holes and cracks.

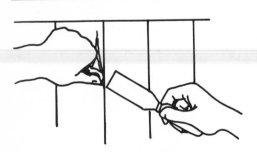

Fig. 8.2d

6. With a dust brush, remove all traces of dirt from the woodwork. Sweep the floor.

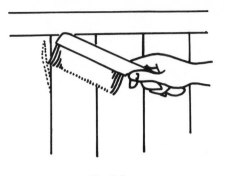

Fig. 8.2e

7. Put drop sheets or paper on the floor. Put ladders in place.

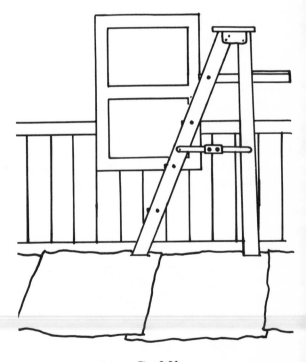

Fig. 8.2f

8. Prepare the paint.

9. Apply the paint. Finish brushing the long way wherever possible.

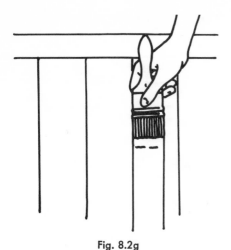

Fig. 8.2g

10. When the paint is dry, remove drop sheets or paper. Clean the floor. Replace the furniture.

Points to Remember About Repainting Interior Woodwork

1. Glossy surfaces should be sanded to remove the gloss. Removing the gloss insures that the new coat of paint will adhere properly.

2. Washing the surface with a strong solution of washing soda and water will help to remove some gloss.

REPAINTING EXTERIOR WOODWORK

The proper way for an exterior paint to wear is by chalking. Chalking is what happens when the surface of a paint turns to powder. This feature is very desirable in exterior paints. A good exterior paint, which chalks slowly, saves a good deal of time and effort when the surface is to be repainted. The paint gradually becomes thinner as the surface of the paint chalks. By the time a new paint job is needed, the old layer of paint is thin enough to take a new coat of paint. All the preparation that is necessary is to brush off the loose powder on the surface of the old paint. If the old paint has not chalked, it must be removed before repainting. If new paint is applied to the surface of a paint that does not have this chalking feature, the layers of paint will become so thick that the paint will crack, blister, and peel.

Steps in Preparing and Repainting Exterior Woodwork

1. Cover with drop sheets any flowers and shrubs that are close to the wall below the working area.

Fig. 8.3a

2. Remove loose or blistered paint with a scraper or steel brush. Brush off any chalked paint.

Fig. 8.3b

3. Sand all the painted wood with rough sandpaper.

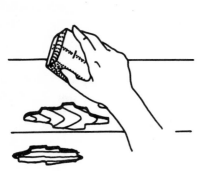

Fig. 8.3c

4. Remove loose putty from around window panes. Reputty.

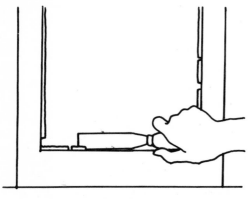

Fig. 8.3d

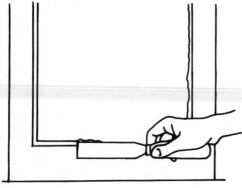

Fig. 8.3e

5. Dust off all traces of dirt and dust.

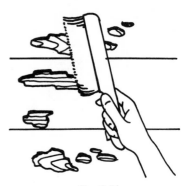

Fig. 8.3f

6. Prime all areas that have been sanded to bare wood. Use a good outside primer. Allow the primer to dry for at least two days.

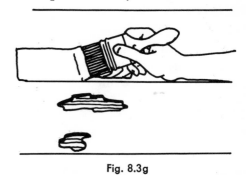

Fig. 8.3g

7. Prepare the paint and ladders.

Fig. 8.3h

8. Apply the paint.

Fig. 8.3i

Points to Remember About Repainting
Exterior Woodwork

1. Paint the higher part of the house first.

2. Be sure that the ladders are in good condition. Inspect ladders for breaks or decay before you use them.

3. Move the drop sheets when the ladders are moved.

4. Most of the loose old paint is found along the bottom of window and door sills.

5. Paint from the unpainted area into the painted area.

6. If you are using oil paint, choose a cool, dry day to do the job. Work in the shade wherever possible. Direct heat from the sun will cause the paint to form a surface skin. The paint will still be wet underneath this skin, and will wrinkle.

7. Oil paints must be applied on a perfectly dry surface. If the surface is wet when the oil paint is applied, the paint will blister or peel. Latex paints are available for outside use. These paints can be applied on surfaces that are slightly damp without causing cracking or peeling.

ASSIGNMENT

1. Why should painted woodwork be washed before it is repainted?

2. How can old paint be removed from a surface that is to be repainted?

3. Why should interior paint not be removed by burning?

4. Why should glossy surfaces be sanded before they are painted?

5. Why is chalking a good feature of exterior paints?

6. What happens if exterior paint surfaces become too thick?

7. What are the steps in preparing and repainting exterior surfaces?

8. What causes wrinkling of exterior paints?

9. Why can oil paints not be applied to a wet surface?

9 PAINTING IRREGULAR SURFACES

Many beginning painters dread painting doors, windows and other irregular surfaces because they have no idea where to start and how to proceed. These surfaces can be painted easily if you follow certain basic steps.

Prepare these surfaces as outlined for new wood if the wood is new, or if it is sanded to the bare wood. If old wood is not sanded to the bare wood, prepare the wood as outlined in the section on repainting interior woodwork.

Steps in Painting a Slab Door

Follow the steps as they are numbered in Figure 9.1.

1. Paint the slab part of the door first. Apply the paint in any direction to cover the entire slab. Once the entire surface is covered, brush across the width of the door. Finish brushing very lightly up and down the entire length of the door.

2. Paint the edge of the door. Brush out any fatty edges.

3. Paint the part of the casing which will be hidden when the door is open. That is the casing on the hinge side of the door.

4. Paint the underside of the frame. If the door opens into the room as shown in the diagram, paint only the part of the frame which belongs to the room. That part is from the door stop into the room.

5. Paint the top part of the casing.

6. Paint the rest of the frame.

7. Paint the rest of the casing.

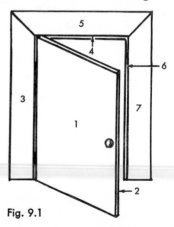

Fig. 9.1

Steps in Painting a Panelled Door

Follow the steps as they are numbered on Figure 9.2.

1. Paint the moulding around the top panel.

2. Paint the top panel. Apply the paint in any direction to cover the entire panel. When the panel is covered, brush across the width of the panel. Finish brushing very lightly up and down the length of the panel.

3. Paint the moulding on one of the bottom panels.

4. Paint that panel.

5. Paint the moulding of the other panel.

6. Paint that panel.

7-12. Paint the stiles in the order marked on the diagram.

13. Paint the edge of the door. Brush out any fatty edges.

14. Paint the casing and frame as outlined in the steps for painting a slab door.

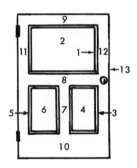

Fig. 9.2

Points to Remember About Painting Doors

1. Keep the door propped open. A piece of wood or a scraper placed between the door and the frame will keep the door open.

2. Spread newspaper under the door.

3. Use a 3″ brush to paint the door, and a 2″ brush to paint the frame.

4. After the paint has started to dry, check for runs. Runs tend to occur in the bottom corners of panels. Brush out any runs with the tip of the brush.

Steps in Painting a Window

Follow the steps as they are numbered in Figure 9.3.

1. Paint all the mullions of the upper sash.

2. Paint the head of the window.

3. Paint both side jambs.

4. Paint the top and bottom stiles of the sash.

5. Paint the two side stiles.

6. Paint all the mullions of the bottom sash.

7. Paint the bottom stiles.

8. Paint the two side stiles.

9. Paint the window stop all the way around the window.

10. Paint the window casing around the window opening.

11. Paint the window apron.

12. Paint the window stool.

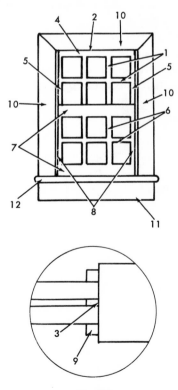

Fig. 9.3

Points to Remember About Painting Windows

1. Use a 1″ sash brush to paint the mullions. Do not get any paint on the glass.

2. The rest of the wood around the window can be painted more easily and quickly with a 2″ brush.

3. Leave the window slightly open at the bottom to make it easier to open the window after the paint dries.

Steps in Painting a Chair

Follow the steps as they are numbered in Figure 9.4.

1. Turn the chair upside down and place it on a table.

2. Paint one of the front legs completely.

3. Paint the other front leg.

4. Paint all the rungs.

5. Stand the chair upright and finish the rungs.

6. Paint one of the back legs.

7. Paint the other back leg.

8. Paint both sides of the back supports.

9. Paint the apron of the seat.

10. Paint the edge of the seat.

11. Paint the seat.

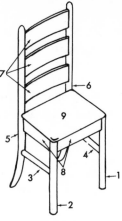

Fig. 9.4

Points to Remember About Painting Chairs

1. Paint the hardest-to-reach parts first.

2. When staining a chair, wipe off the excess stain after each step. If you wait until the entire chair is stained before removing the excess stain, the stain will be too dry to wipe off properly.

3. Do not let any runs form. Keep checking the surface for runs and eliminate them with the tip of the brush before they have time to start drying.

10 COLOUR THEORY AND PRACTICE

SOURCE OF COLOUR

Light is the source of all colour. Where there is no light, there is no colour. In a bright room, a rose is seen in its full colour. If the rose is put in a darkened room, all that is seen is the grey shape of the rose.

Fig. 10.1a   A rose seen in bright light

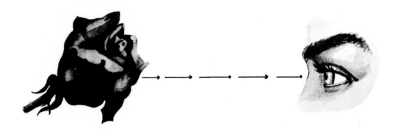

Fig. 10.1b   A rose seen in a dark place

The sun, a candle, a light bulb, are all sources of light. Light from any one of these sources looks white, or nearly white. If, however, the white light shines through a triangular piece of glass called a prism, you can see that it is made up of all the colours of the rainbow.

There is only one way to get a real understanding of colour. You must mix some colours yourself so that you will see what different colour terms mean. One way to mix colours is to mix paint. By mixing several colours of paint, you will learn the meanings of basic colour terms.

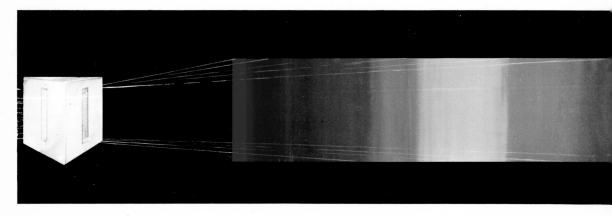

Fig. 10.2   Light passed through a prism

A white object looks white because it reflects all the light that falls on it. A coloured object reflects only part of the light that falls on it and absorbs the rest. For instance, a blue object absorbs all but the blue part of the light that falls on it. If an object absorbs *nearly* all the light that falls on it, it looks grey. If the object absorbs *all* the light that falls on it, it looks black.

COLOUR TERMS

Everywhere you look, there is colour. Books, pens, wall, clothes, everything has colour. The colour of an object is the first thing you notice about it. You notice first that the flag of Canada is red and white. Only after that do you notice that the red parts of the flag are two bars and a maple leaf.

Not all red things are the same red. Some reds are deep. Some are bright. Other reds are so light that they are not called red, but pink.

Hue

A hue is a basic colour. Red, green, and blue are examples of hues. You can easily see the difference between hues. Figure 10.3 shows a ring of colours. Each colour is an example of a hue.

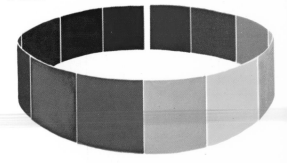

Fig. 10.3   A ring of hues

Value

The value of a colour refers to its lightness. Black has the lowest value. White has the highest value. The greys range in value from the dark greys that are low in value to the light greys that are high in value.

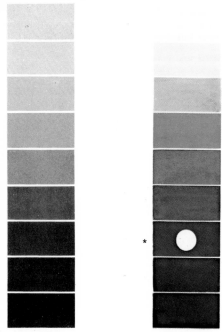

Fig. 10.4a Values of grey   Fig. 10.4b Values of blue

You can make many colours from one hue, by changing its value. To see how different colours can be made from one hue, do the following exercise. You will need black, white, and coloured interior oil paint. The coloured paint can be red, or blue, or any of the other primary or secondary colours in the colour wheel. No matter which colour you use, make sure that it closely matches a colour on the colour wheel. As an example, let us use red.

1. In a small container such as a tin can or a paper cup, mix one ounce of black paint with one ounce of red paint. You now have a very low value of red.

2. In another container, mix one ounce of white paint with one ounce of red paint. The colour produced is pink, a very high value of red.

3. In a third container, make some medium grey paint by mixing ½ ounce of black paint with ½ ounce of white paint. Add one ounce of red paint to the grey. You now have a medium value of red.

Mix two more colours. Make one colour by mixing dark grey (¾ ounce of black paint, ¼ ounce of white paint), with one ounce of red paint. Make the other colour by mixing light grey (¼ ounce black paint, ¾ ounce white paint), with one ounce of red paint.

On a piece of white bristol board, draw and number five squares as shown below.

Paint square #1 with the paint mixed from black and red.

Paint square #2 with the paint mixed from dark grey and red.

Paint square #3 with the paint mixed from medium grey and red.

Paint square #4 with the paint mixed from light grey and red.

Paint square #5 with the paint mixed from white and red.

What you now have is a scale that shows the different colours that can be made with one hue just by changing the value of the basic colour. Of course many other colours can be made by using different shades of grey.

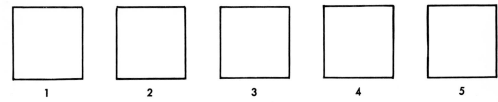

Fig. 10.5   1   2   3   4   5

* The white dot marks the pure colour.

Chroma

The chroma of a colour refers to the colour's brightness. A bright colour is high in chroma. A dull colour is low in chroma. Brightness in a colour is a sign of its purity. A pure colour is much brighter than an impure colour.

Fig. 10.6   Different chromas of yellow

You can make many colours by varying the chroma of a hue of any value. To see how many different colours can be made by varying brightness, do the following exercise. This time you will need only one container for mixing the paint.

On a piece of white bristol board draw and number five squares as was done for the previous exercise. Mix a medium grey, and add one ounce of red. Paint the first square. Add one more ounce of red paint, and paint square #2. Add one more ounce of red paint to the mixture, and paint square #3. Continue the same way for squares #4, and #5. As more and more red is added to the mixture, the paint colour becomes brighter. When you have all five squares painted you will have a scale showing some of the colours that can be made by varying the chroma of a colour, but keeping the value the same in each colour.

Tone, Tint, and Shade

Tones, tints, and shades are made by changing the value of a colour. You make a tint by adding white to a hue. To make a tone, you add grey to a hue. You make a shade by adding black to a hue. Tones and shades made this way tend to be muddy. It is possible to make colours close to the tones and shades you want by adding to a hue some of its complementary colour. Tones and shades made in this way tend to be much cleaner than those made by the addition of grey and black.

PRIMARY COLOURS

The three primary colours are red, blue, and yellow. They are called "primary" because they cannot be made by mixing other colours. All other colours, however, can be produced by mixing two or more of the primaries. For these two reasons, red, blue, and yellow are the most important colours. They are shown on the circle in Figure 10.7.

* The white dot marks the pure colour.

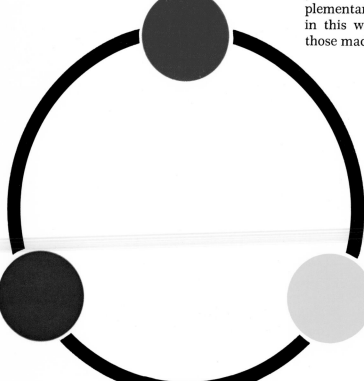

Fig. 10.7   The primary colours

SECONDARY COLOURS

Secondary colours are made by combining the three primary colours in pairs. Red and yellow combine to produce orange. Red and blue combine to produce purple. Blue and yellow produce green. The secondary colours orange, purple, and green are the ones shown inside the circle in Figure 10.8.

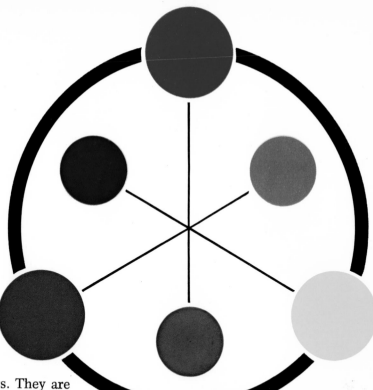

Fig. 10.8 The primary and secondary colours

INTERMEDIATE COLOURS

There are six intermediate colours. They are made by adding a secondary colour to the primary colour beside it. Red and orange combine to produce red-orange. Orange and yellow produce yellow-orange. Yellow and green make yellow-green. Green and blue make blue-green. Blue and purple make blue-purple.

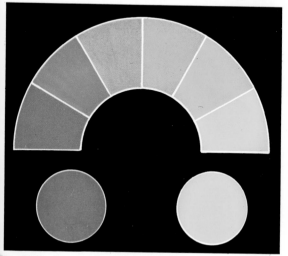

Fig. 10.9 Intermediate colours between orange and yellow

Primary and secondary colours are quite distinct from one another, but the intermediate colours are not so distinct. For example, there can be several blue-greens, ranging from nearly green to nearly blue.

THE COLOUR WHEEL

The colour wheel is made of the primary, secondary, and intermediate colours plus their tints and tones. The primary and secondary colours are shown in the circles on the wheel. The intermediate colours are the ones between the circles. As you can see, the colour wheel shows four different colours between each circle. These colours are all intermediate colours.

The tints are shown on the outside of the wheel. The tones are shown on the inside of the wheel.

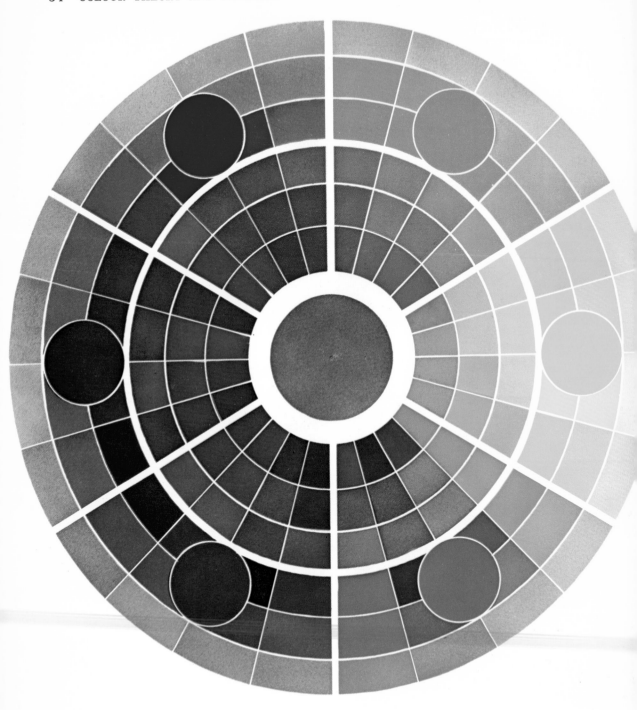

Fig. 10.10 The colour wheel

The colour wheel shows all of the important relationships between colours. With the use of a colour wheel, you can select any of the proper combinations of colours for decorating a room.

COLOUR HARMONY

There are no hard and fast rules for the use of colour in decorating. Any two colours, or any combination of colours can be used in one decorating scheme. However, it is important that colours be used wisely. Rooms that have very bright walls become tiring. Rooms that have nothing but dull colours are dreary. Good colour harmony results from the proper balance of bright and dull colours. To help understand how to achieve good results with the use of colour, several types of harmony have been devised as guides.

MONOCHROMATIC HARMONY

A monochromatic (one colour) colour scheme is one that is made of different values of just one hue. Figure 10.11 shows a room decorated in a monochromatic colour scheme.

Fig. 10.11

In order to prevent a monochromatic colour scheme from being uninteresting and tiring, a touch of some other colour can be added to the scheme.

ANALAGOUS HARMONY

Using two or more related colours (hues that are side by side on the colour wheel) to decorate a room creates a very pleasing effect. Figure 10.12 shows an analagous colour scheme. Blues, yellows, and greens have been used to decorate this attractive living room.

Fig. 10.12

COMPLEMENTARY HARMONIES

A complementary colour scheme is one made of unrelated colours. The variety of such schemes is almost endless; however, we shall discuss two basic complementary colour schemes.

TRUE COMPLEMENTARY HARMONY

A true complementary colour scheme is one that uses colours that are opposite one another on the colour wheel. Figure 10.13 shows a room that is decorated with a true complementary colour scheme.

Fig. 10.13

TRIAD HARMONY

A triad colour scheme is one that uses three colours that are equally spaced around the colour wheel. Figure 10.14 shows the use of a triad colour scheme in a room.

Points to Remember when Planning a Colour Scheme

1. Reds, yellows, and oranges are known as warm colours. Such colours should be used in rooms where the windows face north. Most colours can be warmed by adding a little red. To warm green, add a little yellow.

2. Blues, greens, blue-greens, and blue-greys are known as cool colours. They should be used to decorate rooms where the windows face south. To cool a colour, add a little blue.

3. To make a large room look smaller, paint it a dark or deep colour.

4. To make a small room look larger, paint it a very light colour.

5. A long rectangular room can be made to look shorter and wider by painting the ceiling and two end walls a darker colour than the two side walls.

6. To soften a colour, add a little of its opposite colour or black or grey.

7. Green is the most restful colour.

8. Red is the most exciting colour.

9. The higher a colour is in chroma, the less it should be used.

Fig. 10.14

11 PAINTING PLASTER

REPARING NEW PLASTER FOR PAINTING

here are two points to remember about preparing plaster for painting. The plaster must be dry, and it must be neutralized. If the plaster is not dry before paint is applied, the paint will blister and peel. There are several ways to check the plaster for dryness.

1. Rub the edge of a quarter on the surface of the plaster. If a black mark is left on the plaster the plaster is dry.

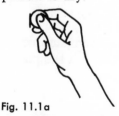

Fig. 11.1a

2. Strike a household match on the plaster. If the match lights, the plaster is dry.

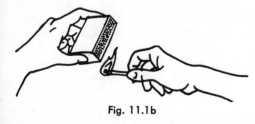

Fig. 11.1b

3. Use a moisture meter. A moisture meter will tell you exactly what the moisture content of the plaster is. Such meters are expensive, but they can often be borrowed from a paint manufacturer.

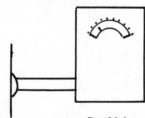

Fig. 11.1c

Plaster is usually made from plaster of Paris and lime. The lime is an alkali that should be neutralized before paint is applied. There are three ways to neutralize plaster.

1. Time alone will do the job. If plaster is allowed to age for at least one year before painting, it will be neutralized.

2. Apply a solution of vinegar and water to the plaster. The solution should be ½ water and ½ vinegar.

3. Dissolve three pounds of zinc sulphate crystals in a gallon of warm water. Apply the solution to the plastered surfaces.

After applying either of the last two solutions, allow the surface to dry at least 48 hours.

It is very important to prepare plaster properly before applying paint. If the plaster is not properly prepared, the job will be ruined.

TOOLS
Very fine sandpaper
Putty knife
Scrapers
Drop sheets
Duster
Ladders

MATERIALS
Patching plaster

Steps in Preparing New Plaster for Painting

1. Make sure the plaster is dry.
2. Cover the floor with drop sheets.
3. Mix patching plaster, in the following way. On a board, form a ring of dry plaster. In the centre of the ring, pour enough water to fill the centre. With a scraper, lift the dry plaster from outside of the ring into the water. Repeat this motion until a soft, workable paste is made.

Fig. 11.2a

4. Patch all holes and cracks. Large cracks should be opened with a screwdriver before they are patched. When patching plaster dries, it shrinks. Large holes and cracks may have to be patched twice.

5. Fill any openings between the wall and the baseboard, window casings, and door casings.

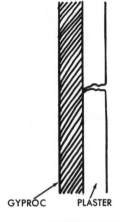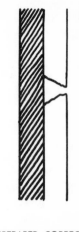

GYPROC   PLASTER

ORIGINAL CRACK   PREPARED CORRECT

Fig. 11.2b

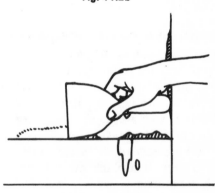

Fig. 11.2c

6. With the broad scraper, remove an splashes of plaster that the plasterer has lef

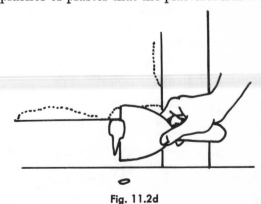

Fig. 11.2d

7. Sand rough spots with very fine sandpaper.

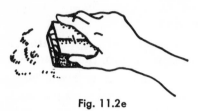

Fig. 11.2e

8. Neutralize the plaster.

9. Allow the walls to dry at least two days before painting.

Points to Remember About Preparing Plaster for Painting

1. Patching plaster can be purchased already packaged. Add only enough water to the dry plaster to form a soft paste. Do not try to remix patching plaster that has hardened.

2. When wallpapered walls are to be painted, strip off the paper and treat the walls as if they were new. It is not necessary to neutralize the plaster.

PAINTING PLASTER SURFACES

The best way to apply paint to a plaster wall or ceiling is by roller. Rollers save a great deal of time and energy. Follow the steps that are listed in the section on rolling techniques.

Use only the best primer for the first coat. After the prime coat is dry, apply an undercoat that is as close as possible to the colour of the finish coat that is to be applied. Allow the under coat to dry, and then roll on the finish coat.

REPAINTING PAINTED PLASTER WALLS

Repainting painted paster walls is not a difficult job. If the walls are in good condition, one coat of paint will be enough.

Remove as much furniture, pictures, and ornaments as possible from the room, so that you will be able to see how much preparation will be needed before you apply the paint.

Wash kitchen and bathroom walls to remove grease and oil. Wash walls in other areas if they are dirty.

TOOLS	MATERIALS
Pails	Washing soda and
Fine sandpaper	water
Putty knife	Patching plaster
Scraper	Primer
Drop sheets	Thinners
Dusters	Paint
Ladders	
Paint pots	
Brushes	
Rollers	
Roller tray	
Rags	

Steps in Repainting Painted Plaster Walls

1. Remove from the room all pictures, drapes, and as much furniture as possible.

2. Push the rest of the furniture into the middle of the room. Cover the furniture and floor with drop sheets.

3. Remove electrical wall plates and other wall fixtures that are not to be painted. Loosen ceiling fixtures if they are not to be painted.

4. Wash the walls with washing soda. Add one handful of washing soda to one gallon of warm water. Wash from the baseboard up, so that streaks will not be formed when water runs down the wall.

5. Rinse with clear warm water.

6. Patch all holes and cracks. Open the cracks if necessary.

7. Sand the walls, ceiling, and woodwork with fine sandpaper. Dust thoroughly.

8. Seal all patched areas with the primer. Make sure that these spots have the same sheen as the surrounding area.

9. If necessary, sand the primed spots very lightly.

10. Apply the finish coat. Allow it to dry.

11. Remove the drop sheets and ladders. Sweep up any dust and dirt.

12. Replace furniture, drapes, pictures, etc.

*Points to Remember About Repainting
Painted Plaster Walls*

1. If a latex paint is used, steps 11 and 12 can be done on the same day as the painting. Oil paints usually need overnight drying.

2. Where there is a great change in colour, or much patching is necessary, use two coats of paint; one undercoat or primer, and a finish coat.

3. One gallon of flat-finish wall paint covers from 400 to 500 square feet.

ASSIGNMENT

1. What happens if plaster is painted before it is dry?

2. How can you check new plaster to see if it is dry?

3. How can plaster walls be neutralized quickly?

4. How long should you wait after neutralizing plaster before the plaster is painted?

5. Draw a diagram to show how a crack should be patched with plaster.

6. Why should walls be washed from the bottom up?

7. A room 12' x 18' has walls 9' high. How much primer will be needed to cover the plaster walls and ceiling? There are two doors and two windows that will not be painted.

12 PREPARING AND FINISHING METAL SURFACES

STEEL AND IRON

Proper preparation of metal surfaces for painting is just as important as the preparation of other surfaces. Metal surfaces have very small pores that hold paint. If these pores are filled with dirt, grease, or rust, the paint cannot adhere properly to the surface. When rust is painted over, the rusting continues. The rust will cause the paint to chip after the paint is dry.

There are a number of ways to clean metal surfaces before they are painted. These ways can be divided into two groups.

1. Mechanical methods for cleaning metal are carried out either by hand or by machine. The hand methods involve the use of a steel brush, sandpaper, or emery cloth to remove the rust and dirt. The machine methods involve the use of power sanders and sandblasting equipment.

2. Chemical methods involve the use of solvents and acids. Solvents such as kerosene, gasoline, lacquer thinners, or benzine, are used to wash off grease and oily films.

After the surface is cleaned, a weak solution of muriatic acid or malt vinegar is applied to the surface of the metal, and is then rinsed off with water. The acid or vinegar dissolves a very small amount of the surface of the metal. Metal surfaces treated this way hold paint better than untreated metal surfaces.

After the metal has been cleaned, apply a coat of good metal primer as soon as possible. Once the primer is dry, apply the finish coats.

Fig. 12.1   Cleaning iron with a steel brush

GALVANIZED METAL

Galvanized metal is usually sheet iron or steel that has been dipped in hot zinc. The hot zinc forms large, protective crystals on the surface, which prevent or delay the rusting of the

61

iron. Galvanized iron is used to make eaves-troughs, flashing around chimneys, and covers for outside exhaust fans.

If a galvanized surface has been exposed to the weather for six months or more, the paint will adhere to it more easily than to un-weathered metal. This weathered condition can be imitated by treating the surface with vinegar or benzine.

Steps in Finishing Galvanized Surfaces

1. Wipe the galvanized surface with a rag soaked in vinegar or benzine.
2. Rinse the surface with clean water.

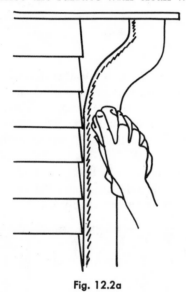

Fig. 12.2a

3. Allow the surface to dry completely.
4. Apply the prime coat. Use a good red lead or blue lead primer. Apply the prime coat as soon as possible after the cleaning is finished.
5. Apply the finishing coat. You will use the same finishing coats that are used on other surfaces. If the metal surface is indoors, use an interior paint. If the metal surface is

outdoors, use an exterior paint. Most metal surfaces will be painted with a brush. Eaves-troughs, for example, are too irregular in shape to be painted in any way other than brushing.

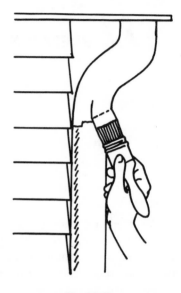

Fig. 12.2b

Points to Remember About Finishing Galvanized Surfaces

1. Iron and steel are galvanized to increase their resistance to weather.
2. A newly galvanized surface is glazed and greasy. If the surface is not washed with vinegar or benzine, paint will not adhere properly.

ASSIGNMENT

1. How do metal surfaces hold paint?
2. What happens if paint is applied over rust?
3. Name two ways of cleaning metal.
4. Why will paint not adhere properly on newly galvanized metal?

13 STAINING WOOD

WORDS TO LEARN

Cross-Streaks — marks left when paint or stain is brushed across the grain of wood

Lapstreak — a dark mark made by one brush stroke overlapping another brush stroke

Tack Rag — a rag soaked in turpentine, dabbed with varnish, and wrung out until the varnish is spread evenly through the rag

Wash Coat — a very thin coat of paint, shellac, or varnish

Gummy — sticky

Tack Off — wiping dust off a surface with a tack rag before applying a finish coat

WOOD CLASSIFICATION

Woods can be divided into two classes.

1. Softwoods are evergreen or coniferous trees. Pine, spruce, and balsam are examples of softwoods.

2. Hardwoods are trees that lose their leaves in the fall. Oak, maple, walnut, birch, cherry, basswood are some of these trees. Because hardwoods lose their leaves in the fall, they are called deciduous trees.

Fig. 13.1 Evergreen   Deciduous

Hardwoods can be further divided into two groups.

    (a) Close-grained woods are the woods like birch, maple, and basswood.

    (b) Open-grained woods are the woods like oak, mahogany, walnut, chestnut, and ash.

The pores of open-grained hardwoods must be filled with a paste filler before they are finished. Softwoods and close-grained hardwoods need no filler before they are stained.

Always use the finish that will bring out the natural beauty of the wood. Stains

63

colour wood by penetration. The greater the penetration, the darker the finish. Paints colour wood with an opaque finish that does little penetrating. Some woods should never be stained. Such woods should only be painted. Experience is the best teacher in choosing the best finish for a wood.

STAINS

Stain gives colour to wood without hiding the surface of the wood. Stain adds beauty to the grain of the wood. A variety of types and colours of stain are available. They are classified according to the solvent used in their manufacture.

Water Stains

These stains are made from dye powder and water. The water is heated to just under the boiling point, and then the powder is added to the water. Water stains are available in primary and secondary colours as well as in wood colours such as oak, mahogany, walnut etc.

To make a water stain, use one ounce of dry powder for each quart of water. After the stain is mixed, it will keep indefinitely if it is kept in a closed container.

Non-Grain-Raising Stains

These stains are made with the same powder

ADVANTAGES AND DISADVANTAGES OF EACH STAIN

STAIN	ADVANTAGES	DISADVANTAGES
Water stain	Does not fade too quickly. Very cheap. Available in a variety of colours. Penetrates surface evenly and deeply.	Water raises grain of wood. Difficult to apply with a brush.
Non-grain-raising stain	Does not raise grain of wood. Dries quickly to give a fast finish. Has same colour permanence as water stain.	Difficult to apply with a brush. Costly in comparison with water stain.
Penetrating oil stain	Easy to work with. Does not raise grain.	Bleeds through finishing coats. Fades quickly if not protected with a proper finish.
Pigmented oil or wiping stain	Colours are of a permanent nature. Any colour can be made. Very easy to work with. Can be applied with a spray gun, brush, or rag.	Must be stirred constantly. Tends to cover the pattern of the grain. Clogs pores of open-grained woods.
Spirit stain	Dries very quickly. Can be coated with finish coats almost immediately after staining.	Bleeds through finishing coats.* Fades very quickly. Available in wood colours only.

* This applies only to home-made spirit stains. Factory-made spirit stains do not bleed.

as water stains, but they have a solvent other than water. This solvent does not raise the grain of the wood and thus eliminates some sanding. Non-grain-raising stains, which dry very quickly, are best applied with a spray gun.

Penetrating Oil Stains

Penetrating oil stains are made from a stain powder or dye dissolved in turpentine, naphtha, benzol, or other light oil. These stains bleed through coatings put on top of them, causing the decorator some grief if the surface has to be painted at some later time.

Pigmented Oil or Wiping Stains

These stains are actually thinned oil paint. Any oil paint thinned with turpentine to a watery consistency can be used as a wiping stain. These stains can also be purchased in read-to-use form. Wiping stains are excellent for use on close-grained woods. Because the colouring matter in these stains is a pigment, rather than a dye, these stains have a tendency to hide the grain of the wood. Wiping stains should never be used on open-grained wood because the finish will appear muddy. Pigmented oil stains can be prepared in any desired colour.

Spirit Stains

Spirit stains are made from dye powder mixed with alcohol or acetone. Because spirit stains dry very quickly, they are best applied with a spray gun. Spirit stains can be bought ready-mixed or in dry form. To make a spirit stain, mix one ounce of powder with one quart of the solvent. To make a light stain, add extra solvent. To make a dark stain, add extra powder. Shellac or lacquer is sometimes added to the stain to bind the pigment. Spirit stains fade very rapidly if they are exposed to strong light.

WOODFILLER

Filler is a specially pigmented paint made for filling the pores in open-grained woods before a finish coat is applied. Filling is essential to an excellent finish on open-grained wood. It not only brings out the beauty in the wood; it also helps to prevent moisture from entering the wood.

Steps in Applying Woodfiller

1. Apply a wash coat of shellac over the new wood to make it easy to do a neat, clean job of wiping off any excess filler.

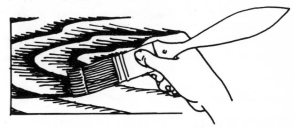

Fig. 13.2a

2. Sand the surface with very fine sandpaper.

Fig. 13.2b

3. Brush the filler into the pores of the wood with a stiff paint brush.

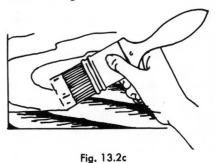

Fig. 13.2c

4. Allow the filler to dry to a dull sheen.

5. Wipe off excess filler across the grain of wood. Use burlap or similar coarse material for wiping.

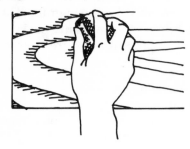

Fig. 13.2d

6. With a soft cloth, finish wiping with the grain of the wood to remove any cross streaks.

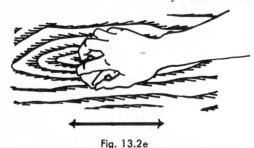

Fig. 13.2e

Points to Remember About Applying Woodfiller

1. Do not apply the filler over too large an area. The filler may set up too quickly and will be difficult to remove.

2. Wrap a piece of cloth around a pointed stick to clean excess filler from corners and crevices.

3. Most fillers can be purchased ready-made and in a variety of wood colours. Some decorators prefer to make their own filler by using the following formula:

12 parts boiled linseed oil
 6 parts drier
 1 part turpentine

Enough silex to make a filler of desired consistency. (Silex is a form of silica which is made by crushing flint.)

One quart of this mixture will cover about 80 square feet.

APPLICATION OF STAINS

Before any type of stain is applied, the surface of the wood must be free of all pencil, grease, and finger marks. Pencil and finger marks can be sanded off. Grease marks should be washed off with benzine or alcohol.

Water stain

TOOLS	MATERIALS
Sponges	Water
Pails	Dye
Brush or spray gun	
Very fine sandpaper	
Duster	
Rags	

Steps in Applying Water Stains

1. Dampen the surface of the wood with clear water to raise the grain of the wood.

Fig. 13.3a

2. When the wood is dry, sand the surface with very fine sandpaper, and dust off.

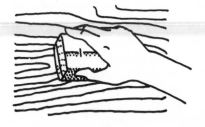

Fig. 13.3b

3. Heat water to just under boiling point.

Fig. 13.3c

4. Add the hot water to the dye powder to make the stain.

Fig. 13.3d

5. When the stain is cool, apply the stain with the grain of the wood. Do not apply stain again to any part of the surface where the stain has dried. If you do, the surface will become too dark.

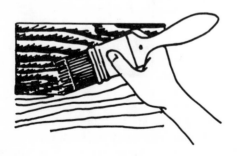

Fig. 13.3e

6. Let the water stain dry at least 12 hours before applying any other coats over it.

7. Apply a wash coat of shellac. When the shellac is dry, sand with very fine sandpaper to remove any traces of raised grain.

Fig. 13.3f

Fig. 13.3g

Points to Remember About Applying Water Stains

1. Sometimes the surface needs two or three dampenings with water, alternated with sandings to remove raised grain.

2. Some decorators apply water stain over a dampened surface to eliminate any lap streaks.

3. For deep colour, apply the stain while it is warm, or apply two coats of stain. For light colour, add more water to the powder.

Non-Grain-Raising Stains

Non-grain-raising stains are best applied with a spray gun because they dry very quickly. If the stain is applied with a brush, be careful to keep a wet edge. If wet stain overlaps a stained edge that is already dry, streaks will show on the surface.

Steps in Applying Non-Grain-Raising Stains

1. Clean the surface of all grease, oil, and pencil marks.

2. Apply the stain first to the areas that are most difficult to reach.

3. If a brush is used, wipe off excess stain before the stain sets up. If a spray gun is used, keep the gun farther back from the surface than is normal. It is better to spray the surface twice than to try to wipe off excess stain that has been sprayed on.

4. Allow the stain to dry as long as the manufacturer recommends before applying any finishing coats.

Points to Remember About Applying Non-Grain-Raising Stains

1. By spraying more on the lighter portions of the surface and less on the darker portions, a more uniform colour is obtained.

2. Always work in a well-lighted area so that you will be able to see spots that you have missed.

Penetrating Oil Stains

Penetrating oil stains are especially suitable for staining softwoods. These stains can be used to make softwoods look like hardwoods such as oak, walnut, or mahogany. Penetrating oil stains also help to hide any defects in the grain of the wood.

Steps in Applying Penetrating Oil Stains

1. Make sure that the surface is clean and dust-free.

2. Apply the stain first to the areas that are most difficult to reach.

3. Wipe off any surplus stain with a rag before the stain sets up. Wipe the stain off so that each piece of wood being stained will be the same colour.

4. Always apply penetrating oil stain *with* the grain of the wood. If the stain is brushed across the grain, cross-streaks will occur.

Points to Remember About Applying Penetrating Oil Stain

1. For a dark finish, apply two coats of stain. For a light finish, wipe off excess stain right after the stain is applied. You can also get a light finish by immediately wiping off excess stain with a rag soaked in turpentine.

2. This type of stain is easier to work with than water or non-grain-raising stains.

Pigmented Oil or Wiping Stains

Pigmented oil or wiping stains are the easiest stains to work with, because they dry slowly. Hours after the stain has been applied, the excess stain can be wiped off with a rag soaked in turpentine.

Steps in Applying Pigmented Oil or Wiping Stains

1. Sand off all pencil and finger marks. Do not sand across the grain of the wood. Dust off the surface.

2. Stir the stain well to prevent the pigments from settling to the bottom of the stain.

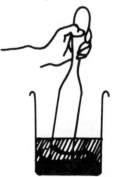

Fig. 13.4

3. Apply the stain heavily with a stiff brush. Do not leave any bare spots.

4. Allow the stain to dry 2 to 8 minutes, or until the stain starts to appear dull.

5. Wipe off excess stain with a clean rag. To remove excess stain from corners, use a rag wrapped around a pointed stick.

6. Finish wiping with a soft rag in the direction of the grain of the wood.

7. Let the surface dry overnight before coating with any finishing material.

Points to Remember About Applying Pigmented Oil or Wiping Stains

1. Rags used to wipe off the excess stain should be put in a closed metal container and thrown away. If the rags are thrown in a pile in the open, there is danger that they will catch fire.

2. If the stain is wiped too soon, the finish may be too light.

3. If the stain is left too long before the excess stain is wiped off, the stain will get gummy. If this happens, the excess can be wiped off with a rag soaked in turpentine.

Spirit Stains

Spirit stains are best applied with a spray gun. When it is necessary to save time, use a spirit stain. Finish coats can be applied on top of spirit stain ten minutes after the stain has been applied.

Steps in Applying Spirit Stains

1. Dissolve the dye powder in warm denatured alcohol. The powder dissolves more quickly in warm alcohol than in cool alcohol.

2. Add six ounces of shellac to each quart of the stain.

3. Apply the stain first to the areas that are hardest to reach.

4. To get a shaded effect, spray the entire surface first. Then respray the parts of the surface that are to be shaded.

Points to Remember About Applying Spirit Stains

1. Home-made spirit stains tend to bleed through any number of finishing coats. Factory-made spirit stains do not usually bleed.

2. Do not expose spirit-stained surfaces to strong light until a protective coating, such as varnish, is applied over the stain.

3. Do not apply shellac over spirit stains. The alcohol in the shellac will dissolve the stain and muddy the appearance of the finish.

4. Never warm alcohol directly on a stove. Put the alcohol in a closed container, and then put the container in a bucket of hot water.

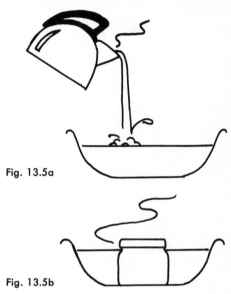

Fig. 13.5a

Fig. 13.5b

ASSIGNMENT

1. What are the two classes of wood?
2. Name two open-grained woods and two close-grained woods.
3. How do stains colour wood?
4. Name five different types of stains. Name one advantage and one disadvantage of each type of stain.
5. What is the purpose of woodfiller?
6. How much woodfiller is needed to cover 120 square feet?
7. How can you get a dark finish with a water stain?
8. How are non-grain-raising stains applied? Why?
9. How can you get a dark finish with a penetrating oil stain?
10. Why should wiping stain not be used on open-grained woods?

14 FINISHING STAINED SURFACES

It is very important to finish a wood surface properly once it has been stained. The stain only gives colour to the wood. The varnish, lacquer, or shellac brings out the beauty of the wood, and protects the wood from damage. Furniture that has been properly finished will last for many years if it is given reasonable care.

VARNISH FINISHES

Varnish makes a very good, clear finish on wood. Varnish finishes are long-lasting, and very hard. Varnish brushes very easily to a smooth film, and can be covered with a second coat in about one day.

Steps in Applying a Varnish Finish

1. Apply a wash coat of shellac if a water stain was used. Use orange shellac on dark-stained wood, and white shellac on light-stained wood. A wash coat of shellac is made by mixing one part of shellac with seven parts of alcohol.

2. Sand with very fine sandpaper. Do not cut through the shellac when sanding.

Fig. 14.1a

3. Fill the pores of the wood with a coloured wood paste filler. Wipe off the excess filler.

Fig. 14.1b

70

4. Apply a coat of thinned varnish (one part varnish mixed with one part turpentine). After thinning the varnish, let it stand overnight before applying it to the wood. Allow the varnish to dry for 24 hours.

Fig. 14.1c

5. Putty all holes and cracks. Colour the putty with colours-in-oil or paint to match the colour of the wood.

Fig. 14.1d

6. Sand with fine, dry, waterproof sandpaper. Dust and tack off.

7. Brush on a coat of varnish at can consistency. Let the varnish dry for two days.

Fig. 14.1e

8. Sand with extra fine sandpaper. Dust and tack off.

9. Apply a second coat of varnish at can consistency. Let this coat of varnish dry for three days.

10. Rub with very fine waterproof sandpaper and water. Rinse with clear water. Allow the surface to dry overnight.

11. Apply furniture wax or polish.

Points to Remember About Applying Varnish Finishes

1. Do not seal spirit stains with shellac.

2. The temperature of the room where the varnishing is being done should be about 70°F.

3. To speed the drying of the varnish, keep the room where the varnishing is being done ventilated.

4. Before applying the varnish, strain it through two or three layers of dry cheesecloth that has been glue sized. Strained varnish gives a smoother finish than unstrained varnish.

LACQUER FINISHES

Lacquers produce artistic and very attractive finishes. Wood can be finished very quickly with lacquers because they dry to a hard surface in 30 minutes to two hours. Because of this fast-drying feature, dust presents no problem when a lacquer finish is used. Also, once the lacquer is dry, it will not become soft at high temperatures, as varnish and shellac finishes do.

Lacquer can be applied over any type of permanent stain. Best results are obtained, however, when lacquer finishes are applied over water and non-grain-raising stains. The woodfiller should be fast drying, and free from linseed oil.

Steps in Applying Lacquer Finishes

The steps in applying lacquer finishes are similar to those for applying varnish.

1. Apply a very thin coat of lacquer sealer, or a wash coat of shellac.

2. With a very fine sandpaper, sand very lightly with the grain of the wood.

3. Apply special woodfiller made for use under lacquer. Wipe off the excess filler.

4. Apply a wash coat of shellac.

5. Sand with very fine wet sandpaper.

6. Apply one coat of gloss finishing lacquer. Allow this coat to dry. Apply a second coat of gloss finishing lacquer.

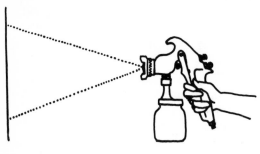

Fig. 14.2

7. Apply furniture wax or polish.

Points to Remember About Applying Lacquer Finishes

1. Because lacquer dries so quickly, it is not necessary to sand between coats of lacquer.

2. Allow the filler to dry thoroughly. The finish can be ruined if the filler is not completely dry.

SHELLAC FINISHES

Shellac finish is one used very frequently because it is easy to apply, quick-drying, dries very hard, and withstands a great deal of wear. A shellac finish penetrates well into the wood, helping to bring out the wood's natural beauty. A thin coat of shellac forms a good base for a wax finish.

Shellac stains easily, has poor water resistance, and has no resistance to alcohol. Table tops, bar tops, or wherever wet glasses, alcoholic beverages, or hot objects might be placed, should not be given a shellac finish.

Steps in Applying Shellac Finishes

Shellac can be applied with a brush or a spray gun. To apply shellac with a brush, use a clean, soft varnish brush. Brush with long strokes with the grain of the wood.

1. Apply a wash coat of shellac.

2. With very fine sandpaper or 000 fine steel wool, sand very lightly with the grain of the wood.

3. Apply woodfiller. Wipe off excess woodfiller.

4. Apply a coat of shellac. Let this coat dry for at least 2 hours.

5. Sand with very fine sandpaper or 000 fine steel wool.

6. Apply three or four more coats of shellac. Let each coat dry at least 12 hours before applying the next coat. Sand with very fine sandpaper between coats.

7. Wax and polish the surface with a good furniture wax. This waxing must be repeated every 5 or 6 months.

Points to Remember About Applying Shellac Finishes

1. Never use shellac as it comes from the can. Always thin it with alcohol. Mix equal parts of shellac and alcohol together.

2. Several thin coats of shellac always produce a better finish than one heavy coat.

3. Do not brush too much. Too much brushing will cause ridges to form, and lap marks will show.

4. When applying shellac with a spray gun, do not use too much pressure. Too much pressure will cause an orange peel effect. A pressure of about 30 pounds is recommended.

ASSIGNMENT

1. What is the purpose of finishing a stained surface?

2. Why should varnish be strained through glue-sized cheesecloth?

3. Why can sanding between coats be eliminated when you apply a lacquer finish?

4. Why should shellac not be used on table tops?

5. Why should shellac not be brushed too much?

6. What happens if too much pressure is used when you apply shellac with a spray gun?

15 FURNITURE REFINISHING

There are no short cuts to a good furniture refinishing job. Each step must be done properly and well before the next step is started. The main steps in refinishing are:

1. Remove the old finish.
2. Prepare the surface for the new finish.
3. Apply the new finish.

REMOVING THE OLD FINISH

To find out which solvent to use to remove the old finish, apply different types of solvent to part of the surface of the article to be refinished. Alcohol will soften a shellac finish. Lacquer thinners will soften a lacquer finish. Paint and varnish remover will soften all oil finishes. Water paints must be sanded off.

TOOLS	MATERIALS
Drop sheet	Solvent
Screwdriver	
Old brush	
Rubber gloves	
Putty knife	
Scraper	
Steel wool	
Burlap	
Rags	

Steps in Removing the Old Finish

1. Spread newspaper or drop sheet under the article to be refinished.

Fig. 15.1a

2. Remove handles, knobs, hinges, and any ornamentation.

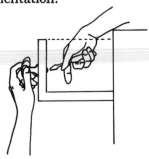

Fig. 15.1b

3. Remove any wax or furniture polish by wiping the surface with a rag dipped in alcohol or benzine.

Fig. 15.1c

4. Apply the proper solvent liberally with the grain of the wood.

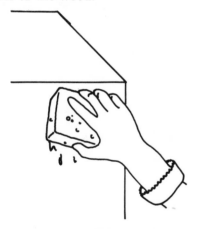

Fig. 15.1d

5. When the old finish starts to bubble, blister, or soften, remove it with steel wool, burlap, a putty knife, or a scraper. Use steel wool on mouldings and round irregular surfaces. Use a putty knife or scraper on flat surfaces. Do not gouge the wood with the knives.

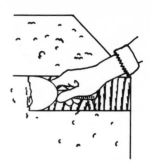

Fig. 15.1e

6. Put the old finish into an old can to be thrown away.

Points to Remember About Removing the Old Finish

1. Some decorators will use only burlap to remove the softened old finish, to prevent any damage to the surface.

2. Make sure that all the old finish and remover is out of all crevices and corners.

3. To remove some old finishes completely, several applications of solvent may be needed.

4. A stiff brush may be used in place of steel wool to remove the softened varnish or paint on irregular surfaces.

PREPARING FURNITURE FOR REFINISHING

It is very important to prepare the surface properly for refinishing. The finish coat will never cover defects in the surface of the wood. Scratches and gouges that are invisible on bare wood will be greatly magnified by the finish. Such defects are especially magnified by varnish finishes.

TOOLS

Coarse, medium, and very fine sandpaper
Duster
Hammer
Nail set
Tack rag

Steps in Preparing Furniture for Refinishing

If a wax-based varnish remover has been used to remove the old finish, wash the entire surface with denatured alcohol. The alcohol will remove all traces of the finish remover. If there is any of the finish remover left on the surface, the new finish will not dry properly.

1. Sand all the surfaces with coarse sandpaper. Sand only with the grain of the wood. Dust off the surface.

2. Sand with medium sandpaper. Dust off the surface.

3. Sand with very fine sandpaper. Dust off the surface.

4. Drive any nailheads below the surface of the wood.

5. Wipe the entire surface with the tack rag.

Points to Remember About Preparing Furniture for Refinishing

1. The broken pieces of glass are excellent to get into crevices and corners to remove the old finish and paint and varnish remover.

2. Make sure that the surface is free of dust, dirt, and grease before applying the new finish.

APPLICATION OF THE NEW FINISH

All the work in preparing a piece of furniture for finishing will be wasted if the finishing is not done properly. Once the surface has been completely prepared, treat the wood as if it were new. Follow the steps for finishing new wood. The type of finish that you use will depend on the type of wood of which the article is made. Follow all the steps for staining, filling, and finishing.

ASSIGNMENT

1. What are the three steps in furniture refinishing?
2. How do you find out what kind of finish is on the piece to be refinished?
3. Why must all traces of the finish remover be eliminated before the new finish is applied?

16 WALLPAPER

WORDS TO LEARN

Chalk Line — a length of string rubbed with chalk, used to mark a line to show where to hang a strip of wallpaper on a wall

Plumb Bob — a heavy object hung on a string to help make a vertical line on a wall

Selvedge — the part of a roll of wallpaper that is cut or knocked off before the paper is put on the wall

Many people, when decorating their homes, do not think of using wallpaper. Even if they consider it, they may discard the idea because they think that wallpaper is expensive and difficult to apply. As a result, their homes are often not as well decorated as they could be.

It is true that the techniques of hanging wallpaper present some difficulties not found in painting. However, once these techniques have been mastered, hanging wallpaper can be just as easy as applying paint to walls. And wallpaper has one advantage over paint: the job is finished as soon as the first layer is applied. There is no waiting for primers and undercoats to dry. The first coat is the last coat.

There are wallpapers with special designs for every room in the home. Some wallpapers are designed to look like wood panelling. For kitchens, there are wallpapers that can be washed. Wallpaper murals are available for halls and stairwells. For dining rooms, there are flocked and embossed wallpapers that can add an impressive touch of elegance. The variety of kinds and designs of wallpaper is almost endless.

Wallpaper, paint, and imagination, skilfully used, will produce the right decorative effect in any home.

WALLPAPER MEASUREMENT

In Canada, a roll of wallpaper contains about 35 square feet. It is 7 yards long and 22 inches wide. Part of the width is selvedge. To find out the number of single rolls needed to paper any surface, calculate the area of the surface to be papered, and divide by thirty. Deduct a single roll for every two average openings. For example, if a room has one door and one ordinary sized window, you would deduct a single roll. Paper is ordered by the single roll, but delivered in double roll lengths. There is less waste when lengths are cut from one double roll than from two single rolls.

HOW WALLPAPER IS WRAPPED

Wallpaper is usually wrapped in one of three ways.

1. The most common type of wallpaper is semi-trimmed. The selvedges are perforated so that they can be knocked off before the paper is cut. About 90% of all the wallpaper used is semi-trimmed.

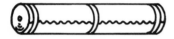

Fig. 16.1a

2. Untrimmed paper has a single tape wrapped around the middle of the roll to keep it from unravelling. Flocked papers are usually untrimmed.

Fig. 16.1b

3. Trimmed paper has no selvedges. The paper is wrapped with a protective covering to protect the ends. Mural papers are made trimmed.

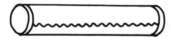

Fig. 16.1c

PREPARING NEW PLASTER FOR WALLPAPER

Most new plaster walls appear at a glance to be in perfect condition to be papered, but a close inspection will reveal defects such as hairline cracks, gouges, plaster splashes, and grease spots. Hairline cracks and gouges should be filled with patching plaster. Plaster splashes should be carefully removed with a broad knife. Grease spots should be washed with carbon tetrachloride and then be given a thin coat of shellac.

New plaster walls must also be neutralized before they are papered. The lime in the plaster will discolour the wallpaper if the plaster is not neutralized.

Before any wallpapering is done, all surfaces that are to be painted should be painted and dry. All the woodwork is painted first, and then if the ceiling is not to be papered, the ceiling is painted.

MIXING AND APPLYING GLUE SIZE

Glue size is used to seal the plaster surface to prevent the paste from soaking into the plaster. A coat of glue size not only ensures an even suction over the entire surface, but glue size also enables the paperhanger to slide the paper into place more easily.

TOOLS	MATERIALS
Pail	Cold-water size
Stirring stick	Cold water
Drop sheets	Hot water
Ladder	
Paste brush	

Steps in Mixing and Applying Glue Size

1. Pour ½ pound of powered glue size into a clean pail.

2. Add just enough water to cover the powder.

Fig. 16.2a

3. Stir the mixture until a brown paste forms.

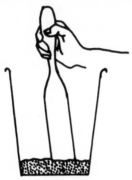

Fig. 16.2b

4. Add two quarts of vigorously boiling water, stirring at the same time.

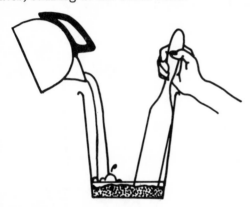

Fig. 16.2c

5. Continue stirring until all the size has melted.

6. Allow the size to cool and form a jelly.

Fig. 16.2d

7. Add enough cold water to thin the size until the mixture is watery.

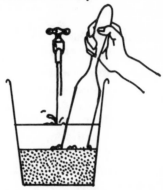

Fig. 16.2e

8. Apply the size to the wall with a paste brush. Do not apply too thick a coat.

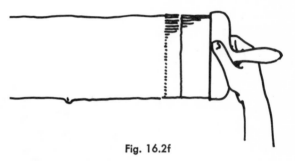

Fig. 16.2f

Points to Remember About Mixing and Applying Glue Size

1. The more cold water you add to the jellied glue size, the thinner and weaker the size will be.

2. Allow the size to dry at least one hour before applying any wallpaper.

PAPERHANGING PROCEDURE

As well as knowing the different types of wallpaper, paste, and surfaces to be covered, the paperhanger must learn the necessary skills to fit paper into the required area. He should develop a routine that he can repeat with machine-like precision. There are some basic steps that a paperhanger must follow, but he should develop a technique that best meets his own needs.

INTRODUCTORY STEPS TO THE HANGING OF WALLPAPER

1. Spead a drop sheet on the floor under the paste table. Make sure that the table is placed so that there is proper light for pasting and trimming the paper. The source of light should be in front of you.

2. Set up the table so that there will be enough room to move around it freely.

3. Place the paste pail in a spot where it will be easy to reach and will not interfere with work. A stand can be bought to hold the pail above the floor.

4. Place a pail of clean water and a sponge beside the paste table.

CHECKING THE PAPER

Before applying the paper to the wall, it is important to check the paper for several details.

1. Check that there is enough paper to cover the full area to be papered.

2. Check that all the paper is the same pattern number.

3. Check that all the paper is of the same lot or mill run. Different mill runs will have a colour difference that will show if used on the same wall.

4. Check whether the pattern is the straight type or the drop type.

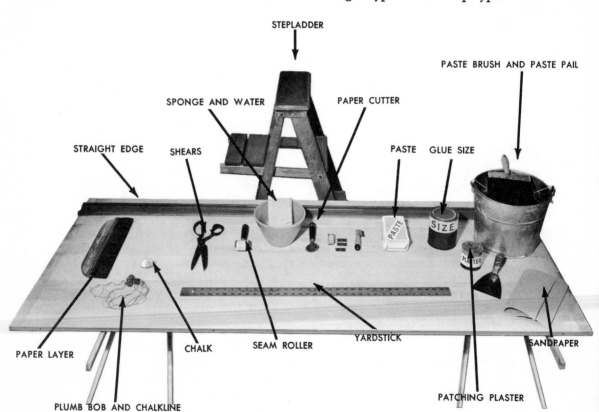

Fig. 16.3 Basic equipment used for hanging wallpaper

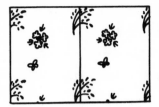

Fig. 16.4a Straight match wallpaper

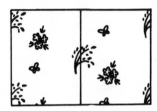

Fig. 16.4b Drop Match wallpaper

CUTTING AND MATCHING THE PAPER

All cutting and matching of the paper is done on the paste table. Do not trim off the selvedge until you determine the match, because the selvedge shows where the matching points are. Use two double rolls for drop pattern paper. Using two rolls will result in less waste.

TOOLS	MATERIALS
Yardstick	Wallpaper
Pencil	
Straight edge	

Steps in Cutting and Matching the Paper

1. Measure the height of the wall and add 2″ at the top and 2″ at the bottom for trimming.

2. Cut through the tapes that prevent the paper from unravelling.

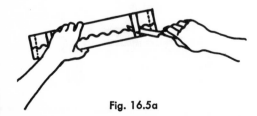

Fig. 16.5a

3. Cut one roll of paper through one match as indicated by the arrows on the selvedge.

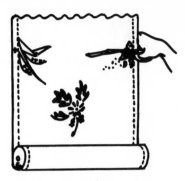

Fig. 16.5b

Mark this roll #1.

Fig. 16.5c

4. Cut the second roll through the opposite match. Mark this roll #2.

Fig. 16.5d

5. Knock the selvedge off semi-trimmed paper.

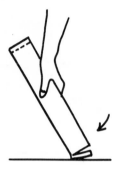

Fig. 16.5e

6. Uncurl the end of the roll of paper. Unroll about 2′ of the paper and let it hang over the edge of the table. Press the paper lightly against the edge of the table with one hand, and draw the roll gently across the top of the table.

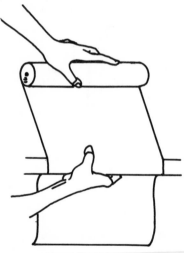

Fig. 16.5f

7. Unroll the required length of paper from the roll marked #1. Place a yardstick across the paper. Hold the yardstick firmly with one hand, and pull the roll upward to tear off the length required. The pattern left at the bottom of the roll must be the same as the pattern at the bottom of the length that was cut off. Mark the roll #1 again.

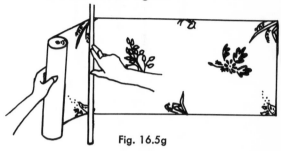

Fig. 16.5g

8. Turn the yardstick lengthwise on the paper to prevent the end of the paper from curling.

9. Unroll from roll #2 the same length of paper as was cut from roll #1. Cut off the length in the same way. Mark this roll #2 again.

10. Keep cutting the rolls of paper to the same length until both rolls are used. Do not cut more than two double rolls of paper, as too much paper on the table hinders pasting.

Points to Remember About Cutting and Matching Wallpaper

1. Keep short lengths for use over doorways and above and below windows.

2. Uncurl the paper as described in step #6 before cutting each length.

3. The top of the pattern should be at the bottom end of the table.

Steps in Turning Wallpaper Over

At first this operation seems very difficult. However, with a little practice, a beginner can become very skilful at it.

1. Place the yardstick across the paper at the top end of the table.

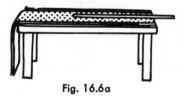

Fig. 16.6a

2. Pull the pile of paper from the top end of the table towards the middle of the table. Roll the paper up on the yardstick opposite to the way that the paper wants to curl.

3. Gently run your hand over the roll, then let the paper uncurl.

Fig. 16.6d

Fig. 16.6b

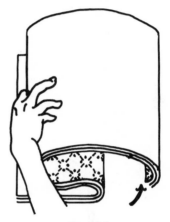

Fig. 16.6e

4. Lift one end of the pile of strips of paper in one hand, and fold the paper towards the opposite end of the table. Fold the wallpaper back to the halfway point of the table. Grasp the folded section of the wallpaper in the same hand. Gently pull the paper along the full length of the table. The end of the paper that will be hung at the top of the wall will then be at the top end of the table.

Fig. 16.6c

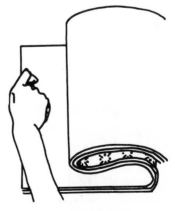

Fig. 16.6f

MARKING THE WALL FOR THE
FIRST STRIP OF PAPER

A completed house represents the work of many workmen. Therefore, it is seldom true at the corners. It is necessary, therefore, for the paperhanger to use a plumb bob and chalk line if he is to keep the paper vertical all around the room. The starting point for the first strip of paper is usually the corner diagonally opposite to the entrance of the room. If there are two windows on one wall, hang the first strip halfway between them. In a room where there is a mantlepiece, hang the first strip over the middle of the mantlepiece.

Fig. 16.7c   Starting over a fireplace

TOOLS
Stepladder
Yardstick
Pencil
Plumb bob
Thumb tack
Chalk line

Steps in Marking the Wall for the
First Strip of Paper

1. Measure the width of a trimmed sheet of paper.

2. At the top of one wall, measure out from a corner the width of the paper less ¼″. Between windows or above a mantlepiece find the centre point.

3. Mark this spot with a pencil.

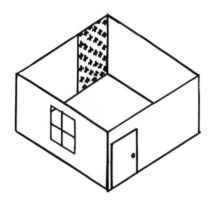

Fig. 16.7a   Starting in a corner

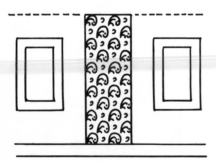

Fig. 16.7b   Starting between two windows

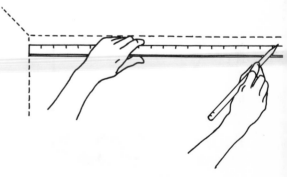

Fig. 16.8a

4. Tack the end of the string of the plumb bob on this mark. Allow the plumb bob to hang above the baseboard.

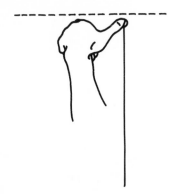

Fig. 16.8b

5. When the plumb bob stops swinging, put a pencil mark at the bottom of the wall directly behind the plumb bob string. Check the width at the bottom of the wall. If the width is more than the width of the paper, the top mark must be moved closer to the corner of the wall until the bottom width is the width of the paper less ¼″.

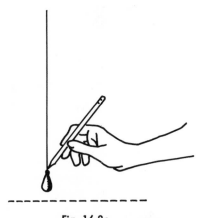

Fig. 16.8c

6. Stretch the chalk line between the two pencil marks.

7. Pull the chalk line away from the wall and then release it. The chalk line will snap against the wall, leaving a vertical mark. The edge of the first sheet of paper is hung against this mark.

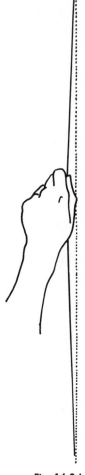

Fig. 16.8d

Points to Remember About Marking the Wall for the First Strip of Paper

1. Take care to pull the chalk line straight out from the wall when snapping it. If the chalk line is pulled to the side, there will be a kink in the mark on the wall.

2. If you chalk the plumb bob line, steps 4, 5, and 6 can be done in one operation.

PREPARING PASTE

Before prepared paste was made and sold, paperhangers made their own paste from winter wheat flour. They placed a pound of this flour in a bucket, poured in a gallon of boiling water, and stirred the mixture vigorously to beat out the lumps. To prevent the paste from turning sour, a small amount of alum was added. Today, modern prepared pastes have almost entirely replaced homemade ones.

TOOLS	MATERIALS
Pail	Water
Cheesecloth	Paste powder

Steps in Preparing Wallpaper Paste

1. Pour a gallon of cool water into a clean pail.

Fig. 16.9a

2. Pour the paste with one hand while stirring the mixture with the other hand.

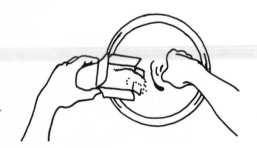

Fig. 16.9b

3. With the stirring hand, squeeze out any large lumps.

Fig. 16.9c

4. Keep adding the dry paste to the water until the skin colour of the stirring hand is barely seen through the paste.

Points to Remember About Preparing Wallpaper Paste

1. If the paste is left to stand for any length of time, cover the top of the paste with about ½″ of water to prevent a skin from forming.

2. Strain the paste through cheesecloth to remove any lumps that were not properly squeezed out.

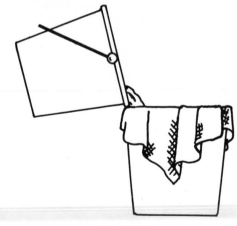

Fig. 16.9d

PASTING WALLPAPER

It is very important that wallpaper be pasted properly. If the edges of the paper lack paste, they will not stick to the wall. If the middle of the paper is not pasted, blisters will occur.

TOOLS
Pail
Drop sheet
Paste brush

MATERIALS
Paste
Wallpaper

Steps in Pasting Wallpaper

1. Place the paste pail under the front right-hand side of the paste table.

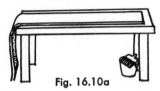

Fig. 16.10a

2. Push all the strips of paper at least 6″ away from the front edge of the paste table.

3. Pull the top strip of paper towards the front edge of the table until the edge of the paper is about 2″ away from the table edge.

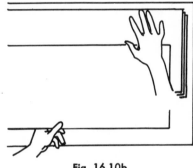

Fig. 16.10b

4. Apply the paste with a brush down the middle of the paper. Brush from right to left.

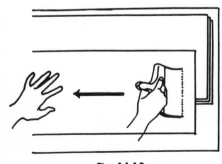

Fig. 16.10c

5. Spread the paste from the middle to the far edge.

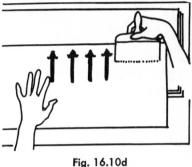

Fig. 16.10d

6. When the far edge is pasted, move the strip of paper towards the front edge of the table until the edge of the paper falls along the front edge of the table.

7. Spread paste from the middle of the paper to the edge near you.

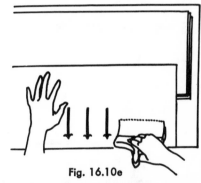

Fig. 16.10e

8. Fold the top end of the paper to the centre of the paper. Pull the sheet of paper along the table until the bottom part of the paper that hung over the end of the table is on the table. Paste this section of paper. Fold the bottom end of the paper to the centre of the paper.

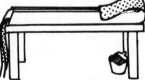

Fig. 16.10f

Points to Remember About Pasting Wallpaper

1. Keep your hands clean.

2. Do not allow paste to smear on the pattern side of the paper.

3. Always hold the paper with your free hand while pasting.

HANGING THE FIRST STRIP OF WALLPAPER

TOOLS

Ladder

Paper layer

Sponge

Pencil and shears for trimming

Straight edge and straightedge cutter for cutting narrow widths

Steps in Hanging the First Strip of Wallpaper

1. Lift the strip of paper and place it over your left arm so that the seam where the two ends meet is on top.

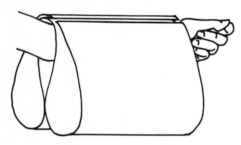

Fig. 16.11a

2. Climb the ladder to the required height.

3. Hold the top right corner of the strip between the first finger and thumb of your right hand.

4. Place the three other fingers under the fold.

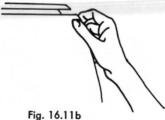

Fig. 16.11b

5. Hold the top left corner of the paper in the same way with your left hand.

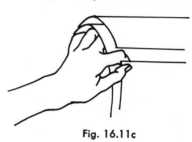

Fig. 16.11c

6. Hold the paper against your body and allow the paper to unfold. If you let the paper unfold too rapidly, it will tear.

Fig. 16.11d

7. Place the backs of your three fingers of each hand against the pattern side of the paper.

Fig. 16.11e

8. While holding the top corners of the paper with the first finger and thumb of each hand, turn the corners of the paper back so that the whole palm of each hand is against the pattern side of the paper.

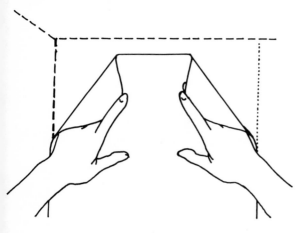

Fig. 16.11f

9. Place the paper against the wall with the edge along the chalk line. The paper will remain where it is placed.

Steps in Smoothing Paper

1. Run the paper layer down the middle of the length of paper. Press the paper layer against the paper gently but firmly.

2. Smooth out from the centre of the paper to the edges. Remove all air bubbles, blisters, and wrinkles.

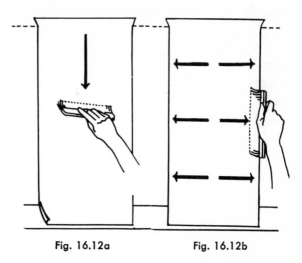

Fig. 16.12a   Fig. 16.12b

3. Tap the edges of the paper with the paper layer to make sure that the edges stick properly to the wall.

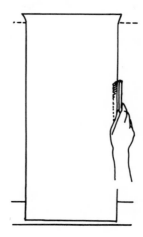

Fig. 16.12c

4. Work the paper firmly against door and window casings, baseboards, and into all corners.

Points to Remember About Smoothing Paper

1. Do not apply too much pressure in smoothing the paper. The paper may stretch, and if it does, you will not be able to match the next sheet properly.

2. Wet paper has a tendency to tear when too much pressure is applied to it.

3. Sometimes, you will have to pull the paper away from the wall and smooth it down again to eliminate wrinkles.

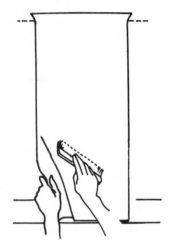

Fig. 16.12d

Steps in Trimming Wallpaper at the Ceiling

1. Smooth the paper right into the corner made by the ceiling and the wall. Tap the paper firmly into the corner with the paper layer.

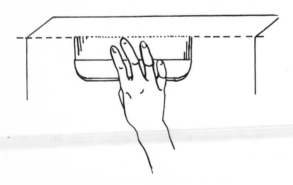

Fig. 16.13a

2. Hold the shears open. Run one edge of the shears along the paper in the corner.

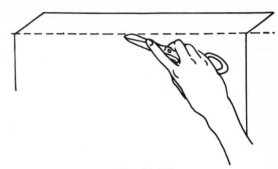

Fig. 16.13b

3. Pull back the paper and cut it along the mark made by the shears.

Fig. 16.13c

4. Sponge off any paste on the ceiling.

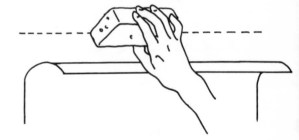

Fig. 16.13d

5. Smooth back the paper.

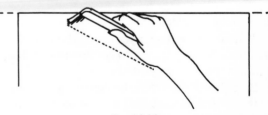

Fig. 16.13e

Steps in Trimming Wallpaper at the Baseboard

1. Tap the paper with the paper layer into the corner made by the baseboard and the wall. Tap the paper firmly enough to make a crease.

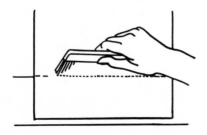

Fig. 16.14a

2. Mark this crease with a pencil.

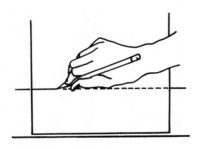

Fig. 16.14b

3. Pull the paper away from the wall, and cut along the pencil mark with the shears.

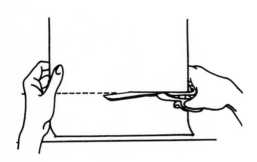

Fig. 16.14c

4. Sponge off any paste on the baseboard.

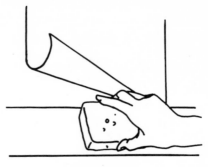

Fig. 16.14d

5. Smooth back the paper. Tap the paper right into the corner with the paper layer.

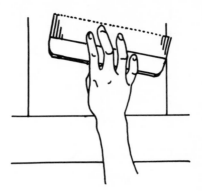

Fig. 16.14e

Steps in Trimming Wallpaper Around a Light Switch

1. Turn off the electric power.

Fig. 16.15a

2. Remove the switch cover.

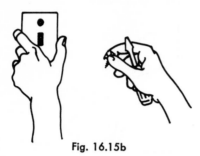

Fig. 16.15b

3. Hang the strip of wallpaper.
4. With shears, cut the paper around the switch.

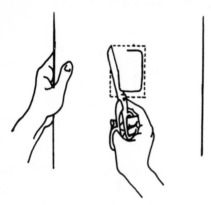

Fig. 16.15c

5. Remove any paste from the switch.

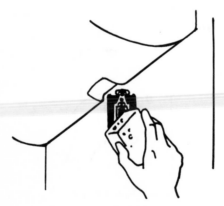

Fig. 16.15d

6. Smooth the paper against the wall.

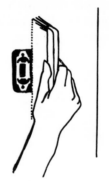

Fig. 16.15e

7. Replace the switch cover.

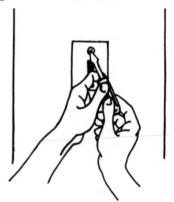

Fig. 16.15f

Steps in Trimming Wallpaper at Doors

1. Smooth the paper against the door casing.

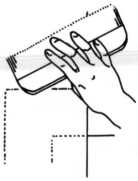

Fig. 16.16a

2. Hold one finger against the paper at the top corner of the door casing.

3. With the shears, make a 45° cut towards the finger.

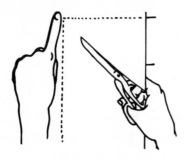

Fig. 16.16b

4. Tap the paper into the corner made by the casing and the wall to make a crease. Mark this crease with a pencil.

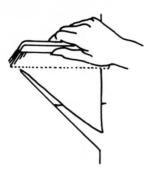

Fig. 16.16c

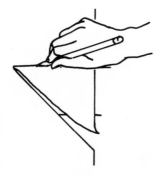

Fig. 16.16d

5. Pull the paper back, and cut along the pencil mark.

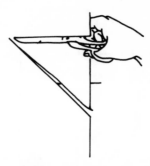

Fig. 16.16e

6. Sponge off any paste on the casing and smooth back the paper. Tap the paper firmly into the corner.

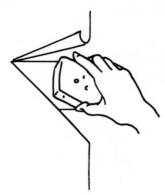

Fig. 16.16f

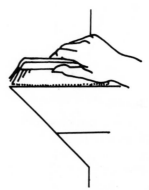

Fig. 16.16g

7. Mark and trim the paper hanging over the door casing.

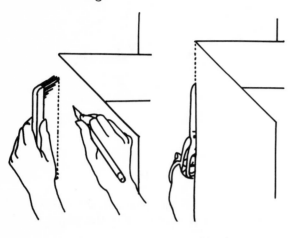

Fig. 16.16h   Fig. 16.16i

8. Wipe off any paste on the door casing.
9. Smooth back the paper.

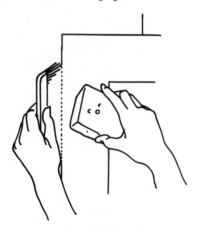

Fig. 16.16j

TYPES OF SEAMS

There are three types of seams or joints that are used in paperhanging.

1. A butt joint is made by trimming both selvedges and placing the edge of one sheet of paper against the edge of the sheet that has already been hung so that the joint is not noticeable. This type of joint is the most common one.

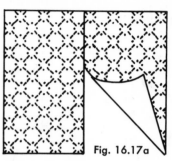

Fig. 16.17a

2. A hairline joint has a slight opening between the edges of the sheets of wallpaper. The opening between the two pieces of paper should not be any wider than the thickness of a hair. This type of joint is used for lining papers. A lining paper is one that is put on a wall before silk is applied to the wall.

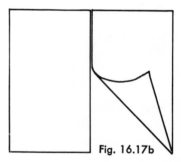

Fig. 16.17b

3. A lap joint is made by trimming the selvedge on one side of the paper and overlapping the untrimmed side with a trimmed piece of paper.

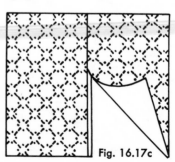

Fig. 16.17c

Steps in Hanging the Second and Remaining Strips of Wallpaper

1. Use the edge of the first strip as a guide to hang the second strip.

2. Match the pattern carefully.

3. Hang the remaining strips in the order in which they were cut from the roll. Use the same type of seam or joint that was used between the first strip of paper and the second strip of paper.

Points to Remember About Hanging the Second and Remaining Strips of Wallpaper

1. The layout of a room will determine where the finishing point will be. It should be in the most unnoticeable spot in the room. The space behind a door, or above a door in a corner are good places to finish.

2. It is not necessary to work only in one direction. When you choose your finishing point, work towards that point from both sides of the first strip.

3. Use short lengths over doors and above and below windows, and make sure their pattern matches that of the paper on each side of them.

Steps in Turning Corners

Do not try to hang a full width of wallpaper around a corner. If you do, wrinkles will occur. Later, when the paper is dry, the wallpaper may crack.

1. Measure the distance from the edge of the last sheet of paper on the wall to the corner and add ¼″.

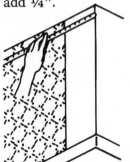

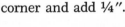

Fig. 16.18a

2. With the straightedge and straightedge cutter, cut the required width from a pasted sheet.

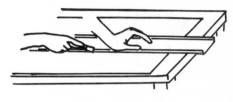

Fig. 16.18b

3. Hang this piece.

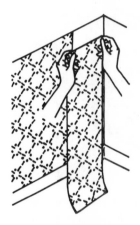

Fig. 16.18c

4. Measure the width of the remaining piece.

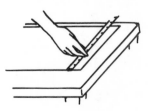

Fig. 16.18d

5. Plumb and chalk a line on the next wall the width of the remaining piece.

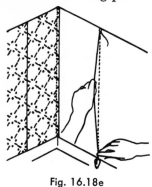

Fig. 16.18e

6. Hang the remaining piece to the chalk line.

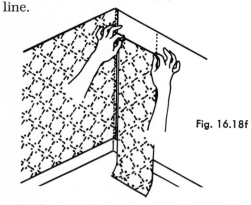

Fig. 16.18f

7. For outside corners, such as a chimney breast, cut the paper so that the strip goes around the corner ¼″, just as for an inside corner. Place the seam on the less easily seen wall.

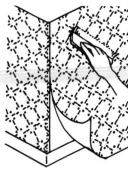

Fig. 16.18g

Points to Remember When Turning Corners

1. Always butt the edges of the two parts of the strip when turning corners. Never overlap, or use a hairline joint.

PREPARING PAINTED SURFACES FOR PAPERING

Painted walls must be carefully prepared so that wallpaper will stick to them. Paint is smooth, and therefore does not hold paste well.

TOOLS	MATERIALS
Sandpaper	Soap or washing soda
Scraper	Water
Putty knife	Patching plaster
Pails	Vinegar
Paste brush	Glue size

Steps in Preparing Painted Surfaces for Papering

1. Wash the walls with soap or washing soda to remove all traces of grease.

2. Sand the walls to remove gloss, as well as any rough spots. If the walls have a semigloss or high-gloss finish, they should be sanded until most of the shine is removed.

3. Patch all holes and cracks. Pay careful attention to openings between the wall and casings or baseboards.

4. Neutralize the patches.

5. Apply a thin coat of glue size over the patched areas.

6. Apply a coat of glue size to the whole wall. Add 2 or 3 tablespoons of vinegar to ½ gallon of glue size. The vinegar will help the size to penetrate the paint, so that the paper will stick better.

Points to Remember About Preparing Painted Surfaces for Papering

1. To ensure good adhesion of the wallpaper to the wall, add a little molasses to the hot water when mixing the glue size. This mixture is very useful on shiny surfaces. The molasses adds stickiness to the size.

2. Wallpaper paste will remove paint, unless a coat of glue size is used to seal the painted surface.

STRIPPING WALLPAPER

Before new wallpaper is applied to walls on which there is old wallpaper, the old paper should be removed. Stripping wallpaper can be a tedious job if there is more than one layer of paper on the walls. Too many layers of wallpaper can attract vermin.

TOOLS	MATERIALS
Sponges	Water
Pails	
Scraper	
Putty knife	
Fine steel wool	
Stepladders	
Extension plank	
Drop sheets	

Steps in Stripping Wallpaper

1. Remove as much furniture as possible from the room. Push the rest of the furniture into the centre of the room.

2. Cover the floor and furniture with drop sheets.

3. Set up the stepladders and plank along one wall of the room.

4. Soak the paper with a sponge. Apply the water to the paper until the paper is soaked right through to the wall. If there is more than one layer of paper, use a wallpaper steamer.

5. With the scraper, try scraping off the paper. If the paper is too hard to remove, keep soaking it or steaming it.

6. While the wall is still wet, remove bits and pieces of paper and paste with fine steel wool.

Points to Remember About Stripping Wallpaper

1. To remove the old wallpaper, use the scraper for the wide areas, and the putty knife for narrow areas.

2. Before repapering, apply a thin coat of glue size after all holes and cracks are patched.

PREPASTED WALLPAPER

Prepasted wallpaper has a special factory-applied adhesive on its back. When this paper is soaked in water, the adhesive softens, and holds the paper to the wall.

An ever-increasing amount of this type of paper is being used by decorators and home-owners. Many colours and patterns are available in prepasted paper.

Directions for applying this paper come with every roll sold. Instead of pasting it, it is submerged in a trough of water to soften the adhesive on the back. Then the paper is put on the wall and smoothed out with a sponge.

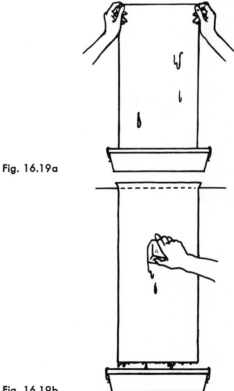

Fig. 16.19a

Fig. 16.19b

ASSIGNMENT

1. How much area will a single roll of wall-paper cover?
2. Draw diagrams to show how trimmed, semi-trimmed, and untrimmed wall-papers are wrapped.
3. Why should plaster walls be neutralized before paper is applied to them?
4. What is the purpose of glue size?
5. What are matching points?
6. What is selvedge?
7. How can you keep a strip of wallpaper from curling after it has been cut from a roll?
8. What is the purpose of a plumb bob?
9. Where should the first strip of paper be hung?
10. When you are mixing paste, how do you know when enough paste powder has been added to the water?
11. What happens if too much pressure is applied to the paper when you are smoothing it on the wall?
12. How do you trim wallpaper at a door?
13. Draw a diagram of three types of seams used when hanging wallpaper.
14. Why should you not hang a full-width strip of wallpaper around a corner?
15. Why are vinegar and molasses added to glue size that is to be applied to painted walls?

17 ESTIMATING

A good estimator is a very valuable employee of any painting and decorating firm. An estimator must be able to figure out how much to charge for a job without either losing the job by overcharging or losing money by not charging enough. When estimating a job, you must keep five factors in mind.

1. Area to be covered.
2. Cost of preparation.
3. Cost of finishing materials.
4. Cost of labour and overhead.
5. Profit.

AREA TO BE COVERED

The area of any surface is found by multiplying its length by its width or height. If a wall is 10′ long and 8′ high, its area is 80 square feet. The fast way to find the area of all the walls in a room is to multiply the distance all around the room by the height of the walls. The area of the ceiling is found by multiplying the length of a room by its width. If there is a closet, you must add the interior area of the closet to the area of the walls and ceiling. When estimating the area of walls, consider the walls as solid with no door or window openings.

COST OF PREPARATION

When you are estimating preparation costs, you must figure how long the preparation will take and how much the materials used in preparation cost. First, you must consider what kind of preparation is needed. Stripping wallpaper, neutralizing walls, patching, puttying, and applying glue size are the sort of thing that you must take into account when estimating such costs. Only experience will teach how long such preparation will take. On the average, however, about 300 square feet of surface area can be prepared in 1 hour. Once you have estimated how long the preparation will take, you must multiply the number of hours by the hourly pay rate earned by the painter and decorator.

Preparation may involve the use of materials, such as glue size, patching plaster, washing soda, putty, sandpaper, and others. The cost of all these materials must be added to the estimate.

COST OF FINISHING MATERIALS

This part of the estimate includes the cost of all coats of paint, and of wallpaper. To find the costs of the materials needed, divide the area of the surfaces to be covered by the number of square feet that the finishing material will cover. If a gallon of primer covers 600 square feet, and if the surface to be painted is 1,200 square feet, two gallons of primer will be needed. If primer costs $6.00 per gallon, how much must you estimate as the cost of paint? Costs of undercoats and finish coats are estimated in the same way. Various types of paint have different prices. The label on the can of paint will tell you how many square feet that the paint will cover.

You learned in the chapter on wallpaper that a single roll of wallpaper covers 30 square feet. If a room has 600 square feet of wall area to be covered with wallpaper, how many single rolls of wallpaper will be needed? If a single roll of wallpaper costs $1.25, how much must you estimate as the cost of wallpaper to cover the room? Wallpapers are available in a vast range of prices.

LABOUR AND OVERHEAD

Labour cost is the most difficult cost to estimate. Some men work slowly; others work fast. Only experience in estimating will teach how best to figure such costs. On the average, however, a painter can paint about 200 square feet per hour with a roller. About three single rolls of wallpaper can be hung in one hour. To find the number of hours needed to do a job, divide the area to be covered by the number of square feet that can be covered in an hour. When you know how long the job will take, multiply the number of hours by the hourly rate paid to the painter and decorator.

Overhead costs include such items as rent,

telephone charges, and wear and tear on tools and trucks. The usual way of estimating these costs is to add 10% of the cost of preparation, materials, and labour to the estimate.

PROFIT

Profit is the amount of money that the painter and decorator expects to make over and above all costs. If a painter and decorator makes no profit he cannot stay in business. A reasonable profit is 10% of all costs. To estimate profit, total all estimated costs and add 10% of that total.

Points to Remember About Estimating

1. Rough plaster walls will need about twice as much paint as smooth walls.

2. An average door and frame will take about one hour to paint and one pint of paint.

3. A window 3' x 5' with eight panes will take about one hour to paint and one pint of paint.

4. To estimate the area of kitchen cupboards, multiply the front area of the cupboards by five.

5. To estimate the area of radiators, multiply the front area of the radiator by seven.

SAMPLE ESTIMATE

A bedroom 15' wide, 18' long, and 9' high is to be repainted. It has a closet 3' deep, 6' long, and 9' high. One undercoat and one finish coat are to be applied. One gallon of each paint costs $6.00 and will cover 500 square feet. It will take a painter 10 hours to apply each coat of paint to all surfaces including trim. How much should a painter charge to paint this room if labour is worth $3.00 per hour?

AREA TO BE COVERED

Area of ceiling	15' × 18'	270 square feet
Area of walls	66' × 9'	594 square feet
Area of inside walls of closet	18' × 9'	162 square feet
Area of closet ceiling	3' × 6'	18 square feet
Total area		1,044 square feet

PREPARATION COST

Time for preparation	1,044 ÷ 300 = 3½ hours		
Cost of preparation time	$3.00 × 3½	$10.50	
Materials		2.50	
Total preparation cost			$ 13.00

COST OF FINISHING MATERIALS

Amount of undercoat needed	1,044 ÷ 500 = 2 gallons		
Amount of finish needed	1,044 ÷ 500 = 2 gallons		
Total amount of paint needed	4 gallons		
Cost of materials	$6.00 × 4		24.00

LABOUR AND OVERHEAD

Total time needed for two coats of paint	20 hours		
Cost of labour	$3.00 × 20		60.00
Cost of preparation, materials, and labour			$ 97.00
Overhead	10% of $ 97.00		9.70
Cost of preparation, materials, labour and overhead			$106.70

PROFIT

Profit	10% of $106.70		10.67

TOTAL ESTIMATE

$117.37

In practice, this estimate would probably be rounded out to $120.00

FINAL ASSIGNMENT

Figure 17.1 is a floor plan of a house that is to be decorated. You are to estimate the price of decorating the interior of the house. Estimate each room separately, and then add the separate estimates together to get a final estimate. Round off the final estimate to the nearest $5.00.

Specifications

1. Walls are 9′ high.
2. Doors are all 3′ wide and 7′ high.
3. The kitchen window is 3′ wide and 4′ high. The bathroom window is 2′ wide and 3′ high. All other windows are 6′ high. The windows marked W1 are each 6′ wide. The windows marked W2 are 4′ wide. The windows marked W3 are each 3′ wide.
4. The front area of the kitchen cupboards is 28 square feet.
5. There are 250 running feet of trim. Estimate only labour for the trim. There will be enough paint left over from the walls to paint the trim.
6. The bedroom walls are to be decorated with wallpaper. Each single roll of wallpaper costs $1.50. The closet doors, the interior of the closets, and the ceilings of the bedrooms are to be painted.
7. The walls and ceilings of the other rooms are to be painted.
8. Every surface that is to be painted will need three coats. The primer and undercoat will each cost $6.00 per gallon and will cover 500 square feet per gallon. The finish coat in the kitchen and bathroom will cost $8.00 per gallon and will cover 600 square feet. The finish coat in the other rooms, including the bedroom ceilings, will cost $10.00 per gallon and will cover 600 square feet per gallon.
9. Estimate the doors as average. They will need 1 gallon of paint worth $6.00.

10. The windows will not be estimated. Each window is just one large piece of glass.

11. Estimate $10.00 as the entire cost of materials used in preparing the surfaces for painting and decorating.

Remember that there is no wall to paint between the living room and the dining room.

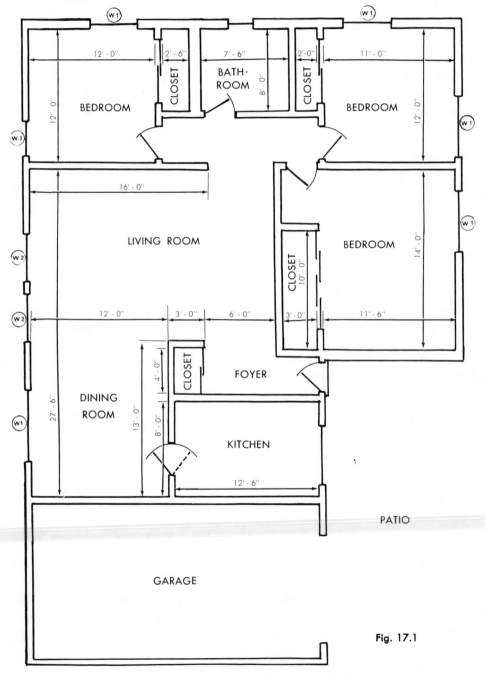

Fig. 17.1

INDEX